THE OFFICIAL COVENTRY CITY QUIZ BOOK

1,000 Questions on the Sky Blues

THE OFFICIAL COVENTRY CITY QUIZ BOOK

1,000 Questions on the Sky Blues

**Compiled by Chris Cowlin
and Marc White**

Foreword by Steve Ogrizovic

APEX PUBLISHING LTD

First published in hardback in 2009 by
Apex Publishing Ltd
PO Box 7086, Clacton on Sea, Essex, CO15 5WN, England
www.apexpublishing.co.uk

British Library Cataloguing-in-Publication Data
A catalogue record for this book
is available from the British Library

ISBN: 1-906358-26-5   978-1-906358-26-6

Typeset in 10.5pt Chianti Bdlt Win95BT

Cover Design: Siobhan Smith

Printed and bound in Great Britain by the
MPG Books Group, Bodmin and King's Lynn

Author's Note:
Please can you contact me: **ChrisCowlin@btconnect.com** if you find any mistakes/errors in this book as I would like to put them right on any future reprints of this book. I would also like to hear from Sky Blues fans who have enjoyed the test! For more information on me and my books please look at: **www.ChrisCowlin.com**

This book is an official product of Coventry City Football Club.

We would like to dedicate this book to:

*All the players and staff who have worked for the
club during their history.*

FOREWORD

I was delighted when I was contacted to write the foreword to The Official Coventry City Quiz Book which has been compiled by Chris Cowlin and Marc White.

The Official Coventry City Quiz Book brings back so many wonderful memories from my time as a player and I will never forget walking through the doors of Highfield Road in 1984 to sign for The Sky Blues. However, my career began some seven years earlier when I joined Chesterfield aged 19. I had only played 16 League games for The Spireites when out of the blue I was told that Liverpool had come in for me. Can you imagine what was running through my mind when I heard that the reigning First Division Champions and European Cup winners wanted me to leave Saltergate and move to Anfield? I actually joined Liverpool around the same time that Kenny Dalglish had just arrived from Glasgow Celtic as a direct replacement for Kevin Keegan who had packed his bags to play for SV Hamburg in Germany. I enjoyed my time at Anfield but knew deep down in my heart that if I wanted regular first team football then I would have to move on. And so in 1982 I left Liverpool and joined Shrewsbury Town where I would spend the next two seasons. Then in 1984 The Sky Blues expressed an interest in taking me to Highfield Road and I jumped at the chance. Over the following 16 years I played alongside some truly wonderful players, all City legends in their own right.

And so to the book ... there is something for every fan in this book; Chris's and Marc's book just about covers all you would ever want to know about the club; the history; the League years; Cup runs; players and managers. What I liked most about the book is the way it is divided it into 100 separate sections with 10 questions per section. And of course what City fan would ever get bored about being questioned on our famous FA Cup winning run in season 1986-87? As soon as I opened the book I was hooked and I know you too will have endless hours of fun testing your own knowledge of The Sky Blues not to mention testing the knowledge of your mates at school, at work, down the local pub or at a game.

I must admit there was the odd question or two that really caught me out; quite a few I should have know because I played in the game!; and several that left me scratching my head because I know I should have known the answer but wasn't just 100% certain.

So in closing, I wish Chris and Marc much luck with their book. It is evident that they have put a lot of time into compiling this book which I know all Sky Blues fans out there will want in their book collection. But a final few words if I may must go to all of our magnificent fans that have followed our Club down the years and in particular to all those Sky Blues who supported the Club during my playing career: Thank You for your most loyal and unwavering support, I will never forget you.

Enjoy the book!
Steve Ogrizovic

INTRODUCTION
By Chris Cowlin

I would first of all like to thank Steve Ogrizovic for writing the foreword to this book. I am very grateful for his help on this project and was truly delighted when he agreed to write a few words. I would also like to thank everyone for their comments and reviews (which can be found at the back of the book).

I would also like to thank Justin Tose at Coventry City Football Club for his help and advice during the book's compilation.

It was nice working with Marc White for the first time, who has been well organised. I really hope you enjoy this book. Hopefully it should bring back some wonderful memories of this fantastic club!

In closing, I would like to thank all my friends and family for encouraging me to complete this project.

Chris Cowlin.

Best wishes
Chris Cowlin

www.apexpublishing.co.uk

HISTORY OF THE CLUB

1.   What is the club's official nickname?

2.   Singers FC was founded in 1883, but in which year was the name changed to Coventry City?

3.   Who was the youngest player to start a match for Coventry aged 16 years, 167 days, against Ipswich Town in 2003?

4.   In which year did Coventry City move to Highfield Road, later leaving in 2005?

5.   Which London club did Coventry play during their first League game at the Rioch Arena during August 2005?

6.   Who took over as club chairman at Coventry City in 2008?

7.   In which season did Coventry play in the European Fairs Cup and lost to Bayern Munich 7-3 on aggregate?

8.   In season 2008-09 the Ricoh Arena witnessed its record attendance of 31,407. Can you name The Sky Blues' London opponents?

9.   When Coventry City won the FA Cup in 1987 which team did they go on to play in the Charity Shield?

10.   In which year was Coventry City given entry to the Football League for the first time – 1918, 1919 or 1920?

NATIONALITIES

Match up the player with his country of origin

11.	John Aloisi	Iceland
12.	Cedric Roussel	Zimbabwe
13.	Michael Mifsud	Holland
14.	Peter Ndlovu	Morocco
15.	Marques Isaias	Peru
16.	Bjarni Gudjonsson	Malta
17.	Martin Jol	Australia
18.	Youssef Safri	Brazil
19.	Ysrael Zuniga	Barbados
20.	Wayne Andrews	Belgium

GARY McALLISTER

21.   Against which team did Gary make his League debut for the Sky Blues?

22.   Gary won 57 full international caps for Scotland but how many goals did he score – three, five or seven?

23.   Which manager signed Gary for Coventry City in his first spell with the club?

24.   Against which London club did Gary score his first League goal for Coventry City in a 1-1 away draw during August 1996?

25.   Gary played in all 38 Premier League matches during 1996/1997, how many goals did he score?

26.   In which year did Gary join the club for his second spell, having joined from Liverpool?

27.   In which position did Gary play during his playing days?

28.   Against which team did Gary score two penalties for Coventry in a 3-1 home League Cup win during October 1997?

29.   Which club did Gary play for between 1990 and 1996?

30.   Gary scored three League goals during 1998/1999, can you name two of the three teams he scored against?

SQUAD NUMBERS – 2008/2009

Match up the player with the squad number he wore during this season

31.	Marcus Hall	14
32.	Guillaume Beuzelin	11
33.	Clinton Morrison	1
34.	Michael Doyle	20
35.	Leon McKenzie	3
36.	Scott Dann	19
37.	Ben Turner	8
38.	Keiren Westwood	6
39.	Daniel Fox	7
40.	Julian Gray	4

WHERE DID THEY COME FROM – 1

*Match up the player with his previous club,
before joining Coventry City*

41.	Freddy Eastwood	Sunderland
42.	Scott Dann	Birmingham City
43.	Michael Hughes	Wolves
44.	Guillaume Beuzelin	Sunderland
45.	Clinton Morrison	Southampton
46.	Kevin Kyle	Walsall
47.	Julian Gray	Crystal Palace
48.	Stephen Wright	Millwall
49.	Dennis Wise	Crystal Palace
50.	Andy Marshall	Hibernian

STEVE OGRIZOVIC

51.   From which team did Coventry City sign Steve in 1984?

52.   Which medal did Steve win with Coventry in 1987?

53.   Against which Midlands based team did Steve make his Sky Blues debut in 1984?

54.   Which top-flight team did Steve make four League appearances for between 1977 and 1982?

55.   True or false: Steve played in all 42 League games during his first season at Coventry City?

56.   In which season did Steve win the Player of the Year award at Coventry City?

57.   Against which team did Steve score for Coventry City during October 1986 in Division One?

58.   Which manager signed Steve for the Sky Blues?

59.   What nationality is Steve – English, Welsh or Scottish?

60.   Against which team did Steve make his final Coventry City League appearances during May 2000 in a 4-1 home win?

MANAGERS

Match up the manager to the season he was in charge at Coventry City

61.	Ron Atkinson	1970/1971
62.	Gordon Strachan	1983/1984
63.	John Sillett	1978/1979
64.	George Curtis	1995/1996
65.	Dave Sexton	1999/2000
66.	Gordon Strachan	1979/1980
67.	Noel Cantwell	1986/1987
68.	Bobby Gould	1982/1983
69.	Gordon Milne	1989/1990
70.	Gordon Milne	2000/2001

TERRY BUTCHER

71. How many England caps did Terry win for his country?

72. Which chairman appointed Terry as Coventry City manager in 1990?

73. Which team did Coventry play in Terry's first game as manager in a 1-0 home defeat?

74. Against which London club did Terry record his first League win as Coventry manager on Boxing Day 1990 in a 2-0 home win?

75. In the summer of 1991 which striker did Terry buy for the Sky Blues from Queens Park Rangers?

76. How many League appearances did Terry make for Coventry City in his career – 6, 16 or 60?

77. From which club did Coventry sign Terry in 1990?

78. Terry was appointed assistant manager to whom with Scotland's national team in February 2008?

79. Which East Anglian team did Terry play for between 1976 and 1986?

80. Who took over as Coventry boss when Terry was sacked as Coventry manager in January 1992?

INTERNATIONALS

Match up the player with the number of international caps he won for his country during his career

81.	Roy Wegerle	102 Caps for Republic of Ireland
82.	Tom Hutchison	35 Caps for Republic of Ireland
83.	Steve Staunton	100 Caps for Zimbabwe
84.	Terry Yorath	41 Caps for USA
85.	Peter Ndlovu	57 Caps for Scotland
86.	Phil Babb	39 Caps for Wales
87.	Ronnie Rees	17 Caps for Scotland
88.	Liam Daish	48 Caps for Republic of Ireland
89.	Gary McAllister	5 Caps for Republic of Ireland
90.	Gerry Daly	59 Caps for Wales

LEAGUE APPEARANCES – 1

Match up the player with the amount of League appearances he made for Coventry City

91.	Steve Ogrizovic	12
92.	Dave Bennett	31
93.	Dion Dublin	173
94.	Robbie Keane	238
95.	John Hartson	145
96.	Keith Houchen	70
97.	Steve Staunton	252
98.	Brain Kilcline	504
99.	Willie Carr	54
100.	Cyrille Regis	172

THE LEAGUE CUP

101.   Which top flight team did Coventry beat 2-0 away
        with Michael Mifsud scoring a brace for The Sky Blues
        during September 2007 in the third round?

102.   What is the furthest round the Sky Blues have reached
        in this cup?

103.   Following on from the last question, which club did
        they lose to in this round of the 1989/90 cup?

104.   Which 'United' knocked Coventry out of the 2008/09
        League Cup?

105.   The Sky Blues recorded a 5-0 demolition of which
        North East club in 1989/90?

106.   Following on from the last question, Coventry beat the
        1976 winners of this competition. Name them.

107.   In 2003/04, the Sky Blues were knocked out of the
        competition by the 2008 winners. Who are they?

108.   Coventry got knocked out of the 2007/08 League Cup
        by which London side that has appeared in two League
        Cup finals without ever winning the cup?

109.   What non-League club were the Sky Blues first
        opponents in this competition in the 1960/61 season,
        the inaugural year of the cup?

110.   Which south coast club became the first club to knock
        Coventry out of the League Cup?.

AWAY DAYS – 1

111. *If the Sky Blues visited Eastlands, what team would they be playing away?*

112. *If the Sky Blues visited Walkers Stadium, what team would they be playing away?*

113. *If the Sky Blues visited Victoria Park, what 'United' would they be playing away?*

114. *If the Sky Blues visited Sincil Bank, what 'City' would they be playing away?*

115. *If the Sky Blues visited Stonebridge Road, what team would they be playing away?*

116. *If the Sky Blues visited the Stadium of Light, what team would they be playing away?*

117. *If the Sky Blues visited Kenilworth Road, what 'Town' would they be playing away?*

118. *If the Sky Blues visited Galpharm Stadium, what team would they be playing away?*

119. *If the Sky Blues visited Moss Rose, what 'Town' would they be playing away?*

120. *If the Sky Blues visited the Shay Stadium, what 'Town' would they be playing away?*

WHO ARE WE PLAYING? – 1

121.   If the *Sky Blues* were in opposition against the Gunners, who would they be playing?

122.   If the *Sky Blues* were in opposition against the Seagulls, who would they be playing?

123.   If the *Sky Blues* were in opposition against the Tykes, who would they be playing?

124.   If the *Sky Blues* were in opposition against the Bees, can you name either one of the two teams that they could be playing?

125.   If the *Sky Blues* were in opposition against the Stanley, who would they be playing?

126.   If the *Sky Blues* were in opposition against the Villains, who would they be playing?

127.   If the *Sky Blues* were in opposition against the Clarets, who would they be playing?

128.   If the *Sky Blues* were in opposition against the Tangerines, who would they be playing?

129.   If the *Sky Blues* were in opposition against the Pirates, who would they be playing?

130.   If the *Sky Blues* were in opposition against the Brewers, what 'Albion' would they be playing?

POSITIONS IN THE LEAGUE – 1

*Match the season with the position Coventry City
finished in the League*

131. 1970/1971   15th in the Premier
                                         League

132. 1975/1976   8th in the Championship

133. 1982/1983   21st in the
                                         Championship

134. 1986/1987   16th in Division One

135. 1988/1989   16th in the Premier
                                         League

136. 1990/1991   14th in Division One

137. 1992/1993   7th in Division One

138. 1996/1997   19th in Division One

139. 2005/2006   10th in Division One

140. 2007/2008   10th in Division One

141. What 'City' did Coventry beat 2-0 on the opening day of the season at the Ricoh Arena?

142. Following on from the previous question, name the defender who opened the scoring for the Sky Blues in their league campaign.

143. Name the 'City' who inflicted Coventry's first league defeat in the campaign.

144. What club did the Sky Blues defeat in the League Cup during this season?

145. Name the Welsh club that Coventry drew 0-0 away to on Boxing Day 2008.

146. Which former Premier League champions did the Sky Blues beat in the FA Cup during this season?

147. In which position in the Championship did Coventry finish - 16th, 17th or 18th?

148. Which seaside club was the first team the Sky Blues beat in the league in 2009?

149. Who scored a dramatic 90th minute equaliser to earn a 1-1 draw at home to Derby County?

150. Which London club ended Coventry's FA Cup dreams?

FA CUP WINNERS – 1987 – 1

151.   Which manager guided Coventry City to this success?

152.   Which London team did Coventry beat in the final?

153.   Following on from the previous question, what was the score in the game, after extra time?

154.   Which Sky Blues player scored Coventry's first goal in the final?

155.   Which goalkeeper played in goal for the Sky Blues in the final?

156.   True or false: this success was the club's first major trophy for 104 years?

157.   Which player scored an own goal, it being the winning goal for Coventry in the final?

158.   Which Yorkshire team did Coventry beat 3-2 after extra time in the semi-final?

159.   Which team did Coventry beat 3-1 away in the quarter-final?

160.   Name the 1983 and 1985 FA Cup winners the Sky Blues defeated on the road to Wembley glory.

BIG WINS

Match up the game to the score

161.	*v. Trowbridge (away),* *FA Cup, November 1963*	*7-2*
162.	*v. Queens Park Rangers (away),* *League, November 1963*	*4-0*
163.	*v. Bolton Wanderers (away),* *League, January 1998*	*7-1*
164.	*v. Bristol City (home),* *League, April 1934*	*5-1*
165.	*v. Rotherham United (home),* *League, November 1925*	*6-3*
166.	*v. Rushden & Diamonds (home),* *League Cup, October 2002*	*6-1*
167.	*v. Scunthorpe United (home),* *FA Cup, December 1954*	*7-1*
168.	*v. Wolves (home),* *League, December 1922*	*9-0*
169.	*v. Torquay United (home),* *League, December 1952*	*5-1*
170.	*v. Lincoln City (away),* *FA Cup, March 1963*	*8-0*

1999/2000

171.   Who was Coventry's manager during this season?

172.   Against which team did Coventry record their first Premier League win of the season, during August 1999 in a 2-0 home win?

173.   Following on from the previous question, which striker scored both goals on his debut?

174.   Which two Moroccans made their debut on the opening day of the season against Southampton in a 1-0 home defeat?

175.   Who finished the club's top League scorer with 11 goals?

176.   In which position did Coventry finish in the Premier League?

177.   Which North London club did Coventry beat 3-2 at home on Boxing Day 1999?

178.   Which team won the Premier League during this season?

179.   True or false: Coventry were unbeaten in the League during December 1999?

180.   Which player was awarded the Player of the Year award at the end of this season?

WHO AM I?

181. I was born in 1961 and my first club was Gillingham. I joined Coventry in 1983 and left them in 1987 after making 90 League appearances for the club.

182. I won a Premiership winners' medal in 1995 with Blackburn Rovers. I made 100 League appearances for the Sky Blues between 1990 and1993.

183. I began my career at Crystal Palace and made 86 International appearances for England at left-back. I joined Coventry in 1991.

184. I was born in 1974 and played for Derby County and Blackburn Rovers before joining the Sky Blues in 2000.

185. I joined Coventry from Wolverhampton Wanderers after making 466 appearances for our Midlands' rivals, and won two League Cup winners' medals.

186. I am a former Ghanaian international who played for Anderlecht, PSV Eindhoven and Aston Villa during my career.

187. I won a League Cup winners' medal in 1991 with Sheffield Wednesday under a future Sky Blues manager. I won 116 caps for Sweden.

188. I played in Coventry's midfield from 1989 to 1991 and joined Walsall after leaving Highfield Road.

189. I joined Coventry from Nottingham Forest in 1999. In March 2009, I appeared in a bathtub in a television advertisement for Paddy Power bookmakers.

190. I broke my leg playing against Manchester United at Old Trafford on 8 April 1996, which effectively ended my professional football playing career.

ROLAND NILSSON

191.   What year did Roland first arrive at Highfield Road as a Sky Blue?

192.   Following on from the previous question, which manager brought Roland to Coventry?

193.   Against which reigning Premier League champions did he make his League debut for the Sky Blues?

194.   In what year did Roland's first spell at Highfield Road come to an end?

195.   Following on from the question above, which Swedish side did he sign for?

196.   In what season was Roland appointed as player/caretaker-manager for Coventry following the sacking of Gordon Strachan?

197.   To the nearest 10, how many League appearances did he make for the Sky Blues?

198.   How many different spells did Roland have as a player at the team in question 195?

199.   In season 1986-87, Roland played for this Swedish club that won the UEFA Cup. Name them.

200.   Name the European Cup runners-up to Nottingham Forest in 1979, which Roland was appointed manager of in 2008.

FA CUP WINNERS – 1987 – 2

201. Who scored the only goal for Coventry City in the 1-0 away win against Manchester United during January 1987?

202. Who captained the Sky Blues to FA Cup glory?

203. Name the sub who replaced the player in Q202 during the game.

204. Can you name the only non-English player to have appeared in the entire line-up for the final for Coventry City?

205. What was the score of the game after 90 minutes of play?

206. Name the 1978 World Cup winner and future manager of WBA who played for the opposition in the final.

207. What Yorkshire ground hosted the Sky Blues' semi-final victory?

208. Name the prolific forward and the First Division's leading goal scorer in season 1986-87 who opened the scoring in the final.

209. Can you name the Sky Blues defender who put Coventry 2-1 up in the final?

210. Going into the final, Spurs held the record for the most number of wins in the competition. How many had they won – five, seven or nine?

MATCH THE YEAR – 1

Match up the event with the year it took place

211.	Magnus Hedman signed for Coventry City	1965
212.	Coventry played their first League match at Highfield Road	1983
213.	Robbie Keane leaves the Sky Blues for Inter Milan	1997
214.	Ray Pointer scored on his Coventry debut	1998
215.	Roland Nilsson was appointed as Coventry manager	1989
216.	Terry Gibson scored on his Sky Blues debut	1995
217.	Peugeot became the clubs sponsors	1997
218.	Peter Ndlovu left Highfield Road for Birmingham City	2001
219.	Robert Jarni signed for Coventry	2000
220.	Paul Telfer signed for Coventry	1919

1980s

221. Name the 1984 FA Cup runners-up who were the last side to beat Coventry in the FA Cup prior to the Sky Blues' 1987 triumph.

222. Who was the Sky Blues manager at the beginning of the decade?

223. Can you name the North East club that were the first side Coventry beat in the 1980s?

224. In what year during the early '80s did Highfield Road become the first all-seater stadium in England?

225. Name the London-based club who became the first team to beat Coventry in the FA Cup following their 1987 triumph.

226. This legendary Coventry City managing director became the chairman of Charlton Athletic in 1987. Who is he?

227. Name the former Manchester United manager who managed the Sky Blues during the decade.

228. Which two times First Division champions from the 1970s were the last team to defeat Coventry in the 1980s?

229. Can you name the boss of the Sky Blues at the end of the decade?

230. Name the non-League 'United' who knocked Coventry out of the 1988/89 FA Cup.

2000/2001

231. Who was the only side Coventry beat both home and away during this League season, winning 1-0 at home and 3-1 away?

232. Who managed Coventry City during this season?

233. In which position in the League did the club finish – 18th, 19th or 20th?

234. How many players did Coventry City use during the League season?

235. Who was the club's Player of the Season?

236. Can you name the three players who finished the club's joint highest scorers with six League goals?

237. Which team did Coventry beat 2-1 away on Boxing Day 2000?

238. True or false: Coventry were unbeaten in the Premier League during August 2000?

239. Which two players scored in the 2-1 win against Southampton during August 2000?

240. How many of the 38 League games did Coventry win during this season – six, seven or eight?

MICKEY GYNN

241. In what year was Mickey born in Peterborough – 1960, 1961 or 1962?

242. In which position did Mickey play during his playing days?

243. From which club did Mickey sign to join Coventry City in 1983?

244. Which Coventry manager signed Mickey for the club?

245. Against which team did Mickey make his Sky Blues debut during August 1983 in a 3-2 away win?

246. How many League goals did Mickey score in his first season at Highfield Road?

247. Against which team did Mickey score Coventry's equaliser in the 1-1 home draw during May 1987?

248. Which team did Mickey play for during 1993/1994 and ended his football career at?

249. Against which team did Mickey score Coventry's equaliser in the 1-1 away draw during April 1991?

250. How many League goals did Mickey score in his 18 starts and two substitute appearances in Coventry's first ever Premier League season, during 1992/1993?

FRANK AUSTIN

251. In which year was Frank born in Stoke-on-Trent – 1932, 1933 or 1934?

252. Which team did Frank join in 1963 when he left Coventry?

253. Which Coventry manager handed Frank his Sky Blues debut?

254. In which position did Frank play during his playing days?

255. How many League goals did Frank score during his Coventry City career – 2, 12 or 20?

256. True or false: Frank has managed Coventry City during his football career?

257. What was Frank's real Christian name, with Frank actually being his middle name?

258. Which country did Frank represent at schoolboy level?

259. Who was Coventry manager when Frank left Highfield Road?

260. How many League appearances did Frank make in his Coventry career – 202, 302 or 402?

GEORGE CURTIS

261. Who did George succeed as Sky Blues boss?

262. In what year did he arrive at Highfield Road as a player in the mid-1950s?

263. Who replaced George as the manager of the Sky Blues?

264. After leaving Coventry, which Midlands club did he sign for?

265. Following on from the previous question, what winners' medal did George win in season 1971/72?

266. What London club provided the Sky Blues' first opposition under George's reign?

267. True or False: George co-managed the Sky Blues with Bobby Gould.

268. Can you name the 1976 FA Cup winners who provided Coventry's opposition in George's last game in charge of the club?

269. At what club, which sounds like the highest mountain in Wales, did George begin his football playing career?

270. Which player beat the appearance record of George Curtis for the Sky Blues?

DIVISION TWO CHAMPIONS – 1966/1967

271. Name the club that played top-flight football in season 2008/09 for the first time in their history, which the Sky Blues beat on the opening day of the season.

272. Which fellow Midlands club finished runners-up to the Sky Blues in the League?

273. Did Coventry win the championship from the team in Q272 on goal difference, by one or two points?

274. Who was the Sky Blues boss that led the club to championship success?

275. During the season, how many League games did Coventry go without a defeat – 21, 23 or 25?

276. Against what 'Town' did Coventry record their highest league win of the season, a 5-0 victory at Highfield Road?

277. Who was Coventry's number one goalkeeper during the season?

278. Name the 'United' which Coventry both beat 2-1 and lost 2-1 to who were also promoted at the end of the season.

279. At the end of the season, this former player from the First Division champions in season 1966-67 was appointed the new manager of the Sky Blues.

280. Can you name the London club that Coventry beat on the final game of the season to clinch the title?

TERRY GIBSON

281.   From which London club did Coventry sign Terry in
        1983?

282.   In which position did Terry play during his playing
        days?

283.   What is Terry's middle name?

284.   Against which team did Terry make his Coventry
        League debut, scoring the winning goal in the 3-2
        away win on the opening day of the 1983/1984
        season?

285.   How many League goals did Terry score for Coventry
        in his first season at the club in his 35 starts and one
        substitute appearance?

286.   True or false: Terry was Coventry's Player of the Year
        in his second season at the club?

287.   Against which team did Terry score a brace in the 4-0
        home League win on New Year's Day 1985?

288.   How many League goals did Terry score for Coventry
        during 1985/1986, finishing the club's highest scorer
        during the season?

289.   Which team did Terry sign for when he left Coventry
        City in 1986?

290.   Which team did Terry play for between 1987 and
        1991?

WHERE DID THEY GO – 1

Match up the player with the team he joined when he left Coventry City

291.	Cedric Roussel	Middlesbrough
292.	Trond-Egil Soltvedt	Bolton Wanderers
293.	Gary McAllister	Aston Villa
294.	Brian Borrows	Bolton Wanderers
295.	Colin Hendry	Cardiff City
296.	Noel Whelan	Inter Milan
297.	Willie Boland	Southampton
298.	John Salako	Swindon Town
299.	Robbie Keane	Liverpool
300.	Cyrille Regis	Wolves

AWAY DAYS – 2

301. If the Sky Blues visited St Andrew's, what team would they be playing away?

302. If the Sky Blues visited Ninian Park, what 'City' would they be playing away?

303. If the Sky Blues visited Sixfields, what 'Town' would they be playing away?

304. If the Sky Blues visited The Memorial Ground, what 'Rovers' would they be playing away?

305. If the Sky Blues visited Moss Lane, what team would they be playing away?

306. If the Sky Blues visited Ewood Park, what team would they be playing away?

307. If the Sky Blues visited The Hawthorns, what team would they be playing away?

308. If the Sky Blues visited Abbey Stadium, what 'United' would they be playing away?

309. If the Sky Blues visited Gigg Lane, what team would they be playing away?

310. If the Sky Blues visited Pirelli Stadium, what 'Albion' would they be playing away?

WHO ARE WE PLAYING? – 2

311. If the Sky Blues were in opposition against the Pilgrims, who would they be playing?

312. If the Sky Blues were in opposition against the Bluebirds, who would they be playing?

313. If the Sky Blues were in opposition against the Cherries, who would they be playing?

314. If the Sky Blues were in opposition against the Cumbrians, who would they be playing?

315. If the Sky Blues were in opposition against the Shots, what 'Town' would they be playing?

316. If the Sky Blues were in opposition against the Addicks, who would they be playing?

317. If the Sky Blues were in opposition against the Baggies, who would they be playing?

318. If the Sky Blues were in opposition against the Bantams, who would they be playing?

319. If the Sky Blues were in opposition against the Exiles, who would they be playing?

320. If the Sky Blues were in opposition against the Yellows, who would they be playing?

DIVISION THREE CHAMPIONS – 1963/1964

321. Can you name the London side that finished runners-up to the Sky Blues, a team beaten 5-1 at Highfield Road on the opening day of the season?

322. True or false: Coventry City won the Third Division Championship on goal difference.

323. How many of their 46 League games did the Sky Blues win – 20, 22 or 24?

324. Coventry beat the oldest club in the Football League 2-0 at home and 3-0 away during the season. Name the club which finished bottom of the table.

325. Can you name the Coventry City boss who guided the team to Championship glory?

326. What 'United' did the Sky Blues defeat 1-0 on the final day of the season to clinch the Third Division title?

327. Name the non-League 'Town' which City hammered 6-1 in the FA Cup.

328. This 'United' beat the Sky Blues 5-2 at Highfield Road in the League. Can you name them?

329. In season 1963-64 Coventry lost away to and drew at home with a team which was playing Premier League football in season 2008-09. Who are they?

330. These 'Rovers' knocked City out of the FA Cup. Name them.

WHERE DID THEY COME FROM – 2

*Match up the player with his previous club,
before joining Coventry City*

331.	Kirk Stephens	Wigan Athletic
332.	Jim Melrose	West Bromwich Albion
333.	Brian Borrows	Luton Town
334.	Leon McKenzie	Celtic
335.	Peter Barnes	Rangers
336.	John Williams	Norwich City
337.	Michael Doyle	Leicester City
338.	Peter Atherton	Bolton Wanderers
339.	Sandy Robertson	Everton
340.	David Burrows	Swansea City

NICKNAMES – 1

*All you have to do here is match the Sky Blue
player with his nickname*

341.	Robert Turner	Snowy
342.	Ernie Toseland	Bugsy
343.	Steve Mokone	Cachete (Big Cheeks)
344.	George Curtis	Killer
345.	Chris Cattlin	Sumo
346.	Ysrael Zuniga	Kalamazoo
347.	Mick Quinn	Leggy
348.	Noel Whelan	Twinkletoes
349.	Brian Kilcline	Spider
350.	Brian Burrows	Iron Man

JIMMY HILL

351. True or false: Jimmy played for the Sky Blues during his playing career?

352. In which year was Jimmy born – 1918, 1928 or 1938?

353. Which London club did Jimmy support as a young boy?

354. In which year was Jimmy appointed Coventry City manager?

355. Which BBC show was Jimmy either the presenter or analyst spanning from 1966 to 1998?

356. What was the title of the song Jimmy wrote whilst in charge at Highfield Road?

357. In 1957 which association did Jimmy become chairman?

358. Which two London clubs did Jimmy play for during his playing career?

359. In which season did Jimmy guide Coventry to the Division Three Championship?

360. True or false: his job at Coventry City as manager was his only ever managerial position in his football career?

BRIAN BORROWS

361. From which team did Coventry City sign Brian during June 1985?

362. In which year was Brian born in Liverpool – 1950, 1955 or 1960?

363. In which position did Brian play during his playing days – defender, midfielder or striker?

364. Against which team did Brian make his Coventry League debut during August 1985 in a 1-1 home draw?

365. Which manager brought Brian for the Sky Blues in 1985?

366. In how many of Coventry's 42 League matches during Brian's first season did he play – 40, 41 or 42?

367. Which team did Brian play for in the early 1980s?

368. Against which London team did Brian score a penalty in the 87th minute in a 3-1 home League defeat during January 1987?

369. How many League goals did Brian score in Coventry's first ever Premier League season, 1992/1993?

370. Which team did Brian sign for when he left Highfield Road in November 1997?

NOEL CANTWELL

371. In which year did Noel take over from Jimmy Hill as Coventry City manager?

372. In which position did Noel play during his playing days?

373. To which position did Noel guide Coventry City during 1969/1970, earning the club qualification for the Inter-Cities Fairs Cup?

374. How many players did Noel use during the 1969/1970 season in the League season?

375. Which manager took over from Noel when he left the club?

376. Which team knocked Coventry out of the European Fairs Cup, which Noel led the team to, during November 1971, losing 7-3 on aggregate?

377. To which position did Noel guide the Sky Blues during the 1970/1971 season?

378. True or false: Coventry escaped relegation by finishing one place above the relegation zone in Noel's first two seasons at Highfield Road?

379. How many full international caps did Noel win for his country, the Republic of Ireland – 30, 33 or 36?

380. In which year did Noel leave Coventry as manager?

AWAY DAYS – 3

381. If the Sky Blues visited JJB Stadium, which team would they be playing away?

382. If the Sky Blues visited Gresty Road, what team would they be playing away?

383. If the Sky Blues visited Griffin Park, what team would they be playing away?

384. If the Sky Blues visited Brunton Park, what 'United' would they be playing away?

385. If the Sky Blues visited Valley Parade, what 'City' would they be playing away?

386. If the Sky Blues visited The Valley, what team would they be playing away?

387. If the Sky Blues visited Selhurst Park, what team would they be playing away?

388. If the Sky Blues visited Ashton Gate, what 'City' would they be playing away?

389. If the Sky Blues visited Whaddon Park, what 'Town' would they be playing away?

390. If the Sky Blues visited Park Lane, what team would they be playing away?

MIXED BAG – 1

391. What caused the Ipswich Town versus Coventry City match at Portman Road in March 1972 to be abandoned?

392. Can you name the 'Nicky' who left Highfield Road in 1984 after playing 53 times for The Sky Blues and scoring seven goals to sign for Birmingham City?

393. This former City goalkeeper was the first player to make 200 appearances for the club despite suffering an injury to his arm in World War I. Who is he?

394. Can you name the former Coventry City captain who took part in an arm wrestling competition organised by Sky Soccer TV entitled Nifty Fifty?

395. Following on from the above question can you name the future Sky Blue striker who was only one of two people to defeat the player in the competition?

396. Prior to becoming a professional footballer what was Neil Martin's occupation – frogman, miner or soldier?

397. Name the London team who were Coventry City's first ever opponents at the Ricoh Arena for a League game.

398. How many of City's 74 games with Ron Atkinson as manager did they win 9, 19 or 29?

399. Can you name the 'City' Harry Barratt played for as a guest during World War II while he was still a Sky Blue?

400. In addition to being relegated from the Premier League with the Sky Blues this player also suffered relegation from the Premiership with Sunderland and West Ham United. Who is he?

JOE MERCER

401. Can you name the two clubs that Joe played for during his playing days?

402. Which club did Joe manage before being appointed Coventry City boss in1972?

403. What award was Joe given by the Queen in 1976?

404. In which position in the League did Joe guide Coventry City during the 1972/1973 season?

405. Which two teams did Joe beat twice, both home and away during 1972/1973, whilst in charge at Highfield Road?

406. In which year was Joe born – 1914, 1920 or 1926?

407. How many full international caps did Joe win for England in his career – three, five or seven?

408. Which club was Joe managing when he guided them to win the European Cup Winners' Cup in 1970?

409. Against which club did Coventry play against in Joe's first match in charge of Coventry during August 1972?

410. During Joe's playing days, did he play on the right, on the left or in the centre?

FORMER OCCUPATIONS

All you have to do here is match the Sky Blue with his occupation before he became a footballer

411.	Mo Konjic	Gravedigger
412.	Stuart Pearce	Accountant
413.	Dave Bamber	Policeman
414.	George Curtis	Financial Adviser
415.	Thomas Gustafsson	Train Driver
416.	Steve Ogrizovic	Miner
417.	Colin Dobson	Electrician
418.	Ernie Hunt	Economics Graduate
419.	Andy Williams	Ice Hockey Player
420.	David Busst	Shipyard Engineer

GARY GILLESPIE

421. At which Scottish club, nicknamed 'The Bairns', did Gary begin his professional playing career in 1977?

422. What age was Gary when he captained the team in Q421 thereby making him the world's youngest captain of a professional football club?

423. In what year did Gary sign for the Sky Blues for the first time?

424. To the nearest £10,000 how much did City pay for his services?

425. Can you name the North East club he made his Coventry City debut against, a 2-1 away victory?

426. In 1983 he left Highfield Road and became Joe Fagan's first signing. What side did Gary join?

427. Name the 'Andy' who awarded Gary the first of his 13 international caps for Scotland.

428. What trophy did Gary win with the team in Q426 in season 1983/84?

429. In 1991 Gary joined this Scottish Premier League side. Name them.

430. In what year did Gary sign for the Sky Blues for the second time?

RON ATKINSON

431. Which manager did Ron replace as Coventry manager?

432. What is Ron's nickname?

433. In which year was Ron appointed Coventry manager?

434. Which London team did Coventry beat 2-0 at home in his first match in charge of the Sky Blues?

435. Following on from the previous question, which player made his debut in the game having been Ron's first signing whilst at Coventry City?

436. True or false: Coventry were unbeaten in Ron's first six Premier League games in charge?

437. What role did Ron take at Coventry when he stepped down as manager at the club in October 1996?

438. Which club did Ron play for between 1959 and 1971?

439. True or false: Ron was awarded the Manager of the Month in his first month in charge at Highfield Road?

440. Can you name the three clubs that Ron managed in the 1970s?

DEBUTS

441. Which midfielder got sent-off on his League debut against Middlesbrough at home in a 3-1 defeat in August 2000?

442. Which manager handed Colin Craven his debut in a 1-0 home win against Spurs during August 1973?

443. Can you name three of the five players who made their League debuts on the opening day of the 1983/1984 season against Watford at Vicarage Road in a 3-2 win?

444. Following on from the previous question, can you name the debutant who scored the winning goal in the game for the Sky Blues?

445. Which future Dutch Spurs manager made his debut during August 1984 against Aston Villa, away from home in a 1-0 defeat?

446. Which defender made his debut as a substitute in Coventry's first ever Premier League game at home to Middlesbrough in a 2-1 win?

447. Which goalkeeper made his debut during March 1992 having signed on loan from Leyton Orient in a 1-1 home draw?

448. True or false: David Speedie scored on his League debut against Tottenham Hotspur in a 2-1 home win during August 1987?

449. Who made his debut for Coventry against Sunderland in a 1-0 defeat in September 1983?

450. Against which club did Chris Kirkland make his League debut in October 2000 in a 2-1 home win with John Aloisi and John Eastace scoring?

JOHN SILLETT

451. Which team did John sign from to join Coventry City in 1962?

452. What is John's middle name?

453. In which position did John play during his playing days?

454. Which manager signed John for Coventry and handed him his debut?

455. How many League goals did John score in his Coventry career?

456. When John left Highfield Road in 1966 which team did he join?

457. Which club was John managing when he won the Third Division Manger of the Year award during 1975/1976?

458. Which manager took over from John at Coventry during November 1990?

459. Which position did John guide Coventry to in the League during 1987/1988, his first season in charge at the club?

460. True or false: during John's second season in charge as Sky Blues manager he guided them to seventh position in Division One, their best finish for 11 years?

LEAGUE APPEARANCES – 2

Match up the player with the amount of League appearances he made for Coventry City

461. Micky Quinn   141

462. Darren Huckerby   314

463. Peter Ndlovu   100

464. Dennis Wise   64

465. Phil Babb   94

466. John Aloisi   34

467. Craig Bellamy   146

468. Tommy Hutchison   13

469. David Phillips   47

470. Ernie Hunt   77

NICKNAMES – 2

All you have to do here is match the Sky Blue player with his nickname

471.	Moustapha Hadji	Cute
472.	Les Warner	Bulawayo Bullet
473.	Steve Staunton	Flying Postman
474.	Frank Herbert	Toffee
475.	John Williams	The Scoop
476.	Peter Ndlovu	Harry
477.	John Sillett	Plum
478.	Brian Roberts	Stan
479.	Ray Straw	Detonator
480.	Mick Coop	Snoz

CHRIS CATTLIN

481.   In which Northern English County was Chris born?

482.   What is Chris's middle name – James, John or Joseph?

483.   At which Yorkshire club did Chris begin his professional playing career in 1964?

484.   In what year did he arrive at Highfield Road?

485.   Following on from Q484 who signed him for the Sky Blues?

486.   Can you recall the year during the mid-1970s when Chris left City?

487.   What seaside club did he join when he left the Sky Blues?

488.   How many goals did Chris score for City – none, two or four?

489.   Chris bought a racehorse named Ajigolo with a former Southampton and England forward. Name him.

490.   Name the only professional club which Chris both played for and managed during his career.

HAT-TRICKS

491. Which forward scored a hat-trick for the Sky Blues against Rushden & Diamonds during October 2002 in the League Cup 2nd round in a 8-0 home win?

492. Against which club did John Aloisi score a League Cup hat-trick in a 4-1 home win in the 2nd round, 2nd leg during September 2000?

493. Can you name the two clubs that Darren Huckerby scored hat-tricks against during 1998/1999?

494. Who scored a Coventry hat-trick in a 6-1 win against Crewe Alexandra in the League during February 2002?

495. Which centre forward scored a hat-trick in the 3-2 home win on the opening day of the 1997/1998 Premier League season?

496. Which 'Peter' scored a Premier League hat-trick against Liverpool in the 3-2 away win at Anfield during March 1995?

497. How many hat-tricks were scored for Coventry City during their first Premier League season, 1992/1993 – none, two or four?

498. Which 'Bobby' scored a hat-trick in a 5-1 home win against Burnley in Division One in December 1967?

499. During 1975/1976 David Cross was Coventry's highest scorer with 14 League goals, how many hat-tricks did he score?

500. Who scored a hat-trick in his home debut (his second League appearance for the club) in a 4-2 home win against Everton during September 1982?

SKY BLUE CRICKETERS

501. This former Coventry legend from 1984 to 2000 played cricket for Coventry & North Warwicks Cricket Club and claimed the wicket of three England Test players – Chris Broad, Alvin Kallicharran and Martyn Moxon. Who is he?

502. He was born in Coventry in 1922 and made his Coventry City debut in September 1946 in a 1-1 draw with Newcastle United. He was an opening batsman for Warwickshire, making his County debut in 1947. Can you name him?

503. Can you name the former Sky Blues' Chief Scout from the late 1950s who played in goal for Lincoln City, Port Vale and Stoke City and who represented Nottinghamshire as a hard-hitting lower order batsman?

504. He was born in Wakefield on 18 December 1933 but rather than play for his native Yorkshire he played cricket for Middlesex. Name this 'Don' who joined City from Arsenal and played at full back from 1959 to 1962.

505. This 'Patsy' played for Brentford, Manchester City and QPR before joining the Sky Blues. He scored on his Coventry debut in 1909 and during his cricket career (Middlesex) only the legendary Sir Jack Hobbs scored more centuries than him. Who is he?

506. He played for City both before and after World War II (1931 to 1948), as well as both Nottingham clubs during the war. He played cricket for Derbyshire and played in the same cricket team as Sky Blues boss Harry Storer, winning the County Championship in 1936, the same year that City won the Third Division title. Name him.

507. This former Coventry City Chairman played 40 games for Warwickshire between 1963 and 1967. Can you name him?

508. His father (Charlie) played for Manchester United while he played for Leicester City and Newcastle United before he signed for the Sky Blues in July 1963. He played wicket keeper for Leicestershire from 1961 to 1963.

509. In 1947 he made his first and only first class appearance for Leicestershire taking a wicket with his first ball bowled. He also scored a goal on his debut for The Sky Blues in 1954. Name this 'Jack'.

510. This 'Robert' was the first County cricketer to play for Coventry City. Can you name the Leicestershire middle-order, right-handed batsman and bowler who joined the Sky Blues in 1914?

MATCH THE YEAR – 2

Match up the event with the year it took place

511. Dele Adebola scored on his Coventry
     debut against Peterborough United   1964

512. Coventry sold Craig Bellamy to
     Newcastle United for £6.5 million   1986

513. Coventry beat Wolves 7-1 at home on
     Christmas Day   2005

514. Coventry moved to the Rioch Arena   1964

515. Ken Hale scored for the Sky Blues
     against Bristol Rovers after just
     seven seconds   2009

516. Coventry lost 8-1 at home to
     Leicester City in the League Cup   2000

517. David Bell signed for Coventry City   2003

518. Coventry paid Blackburn Rovers
     £2.5 million for Lee Carsley   2005

519. George Curtis took over as Coventry
     manager   1922

520. Peter Reid left Coventry having
     managed them for only 31 games   2001

MICKY ADAMS

521. In which year was Micky born in Sheffield – 1960, 1961 or 1962?

522. In which position did Micky play during his playing days?

523. From which club did Micky join the Sky Blues in 1983?

524. Bobby Gould handed Micky his Coventry debut during August 1983 in a 1-1 draw against which London team?

525. Micky scored in only his second Coventry City League game, against which team in a 1-1 draw during September 1983?

526. How many League goals did Micky score for the Sky Blues during 1985/1986?

527. In which year did Micky leave Highfield Road and sign for Leeds United?

528. In which position did Micky guide Coventry City in his first full season as the Sky Blues manager?

529. In which year did Micky take over at the Rioch Arena as Coventry boss?

530. Against which team did Coventry play in Micky's first match in charge in a 3-1 defeat?

DAVE BENNETT

531. At what City did Dave begin his professional football career?

532. Coventry signed Dave in which year in the early 1980s?

533. How many League appearances did Dave make during his time at Highfield Road?

534. In what year did he leave Coventry?

535. After leaving the Sky Blues, what Yorkshire club did Dave sign for?

536. From 1990-92, what 'Town' did he play for?

537. How many League goals did he score for the Sky Blues?

538. While at the team in Q536, Dave was loaned out to this "Town", Name them.

539. Prior to signing for the Sky Blues, what Welsh club did Dave play for?

540. At which non-League club did he end his professional playing career?

WHO ARE WE PLAYING? - 3

541. If the Sky Blues were in opposition against the Black Cats, who would they be playing?

542. If the Sky Blues were in opposition against the Railwaymen, who would they be playing?

543. If the Sky Blues were in opposition against the Robins, what 'City' would they be playing?

544. If the Sky Blues were in opposition against the Mariners, who would they be playing?

545. If the Sky Blues were in opposition against the Yellow Army, who would they be playing?

546. If the Sky Blues were in opposition against the Cottagers, who would they be playing?

547. If the Sky Blues were in opposition against the Citizens, what 'City' would they be playing?

548. If the Sky Blues were in opposition against the 'U's, name any one of the two 'Uniteds' that they could be playing.

549. If the Sky Blues were in opposition against the Stags, what 'Town' would they be playing?

550. If the Sky Blues were in opposition against the Daggers, who would they be playing?

MICK FERGUSON

551. During his professional playing career, Mick played in which position?

552. How many League appearances did he make during his first spell at the Sky Blues?

553. What 'City' did Mick play for when he was loaned out to Coventry City in 1984?

554. After leaving Highfield Road, what Lancashire club did Mick sign for?

555. Overall, how many League goals did he score for the Sky Blues – 44, 54 or 64?

556. From 1984 to 1986, what 'Albion' did Mick play for?

557. In what year did Mick begin his senior football career?

558. What 'United' did he play for from 1986/87?

559. Mick left Highfield Road in which year during the early 1980s?

560. In 1987, what Isthmian Premier League team did he play for?

POSITIONS IN THE LEAGUE – 2

*Match the season with the position Coventry City
finished in the League*

561. 1987/1988   6th in Division One

562. 1985/1986   7th in Division One

563. 1983/1984   14th in Division One

564. 1981/1982   18th in Division One

565. 1979/1980   16th in Division One

566. 1977/1978   10th in Division One

567. 1975/1976   17th in Division One

568. 1973/1974   14th in Division One

569. 1971/1972   15th in Division One

570. 1969/1970   19th in Division One

FORMER AWAY GROUNDS

571. If the Sky Blues had paid a visit to Maine Road in the past, what team would have been the home side?

572. If the Sky Blues had paid a visit to Filbert Street in the past, what team would have been the home side?

573. If the Sky Blues had paid a visit to Highbury in the past, what team would have been the home side?

574. If the Sky Blues had paid a visit to Ayresome Park in the past, what team would have been the home side?

575. If the Sky Blues had paid a visit to Plough Lane in the past, what team would have been the home side?

576. If the Sky Blues had paid a visit to The Goldstone Ground in the past, what team would have been the home side?

577. If the Sky Blues had paid a visit to Roker Park in the past, what team would have been the home side?

578. If the Sky Blues had paid a visit to The Dell in the past, what team would have been the home side?

579. If the Sky Blues had paid a visit to Elm Park in the past, what team would have been the home side?

580. If the Sky Blues had paid a visit to The Baseball Ground in the past, what team would have been the home side?

POT LUCK – 1

581. 80,000 people saw Everton beat the Sky Blues 1-0 at Wembley Stadium on 1 August 1987. What was the occasion?

582. How many teams other than Coventry City have failed to finish in the top six of any of the top four English divisions from 1970/71 to 2007/08?

583. Can you name the youngest goalkeeper ever to pull on a Sky Blues' shirt making his debut in a 1-0 home win over Southampton on 28 August 1982?

584. Can you name the 'Wanderers' who Coventry City have never met in the Football League but did meet in the League Cup in season 1993/94?

585. Name the team beginning and ending with the same letter that the Sky Blues have played in the Third Division, Fourth Division and the FA Cup.

586. This 'Jimmy' played for his country before he made his debut for the Sky Blues, which was also his debut in professional football.

587. Who is the youngest manager ever to have managed the Sky Blues, aged 31 years and 11 months?

588. Can you name the Glasgow Rangers and future City striker who was at the centre of a local radio reporter being asked to take time off work during the late 1970s?

589. Name any two of the three former City players/managers whose Christian name is Noel but was not born on Christmas Day.

590. What player named Best made his debut for the club on Christmas Day 1920 in a 4-2 defeat to Cardiff City?

MIXED BAG – 2

591.   Who is the only player to score in five consecutive games or more for the Sky Blues in the top flight of English football?

592.   Can you name the 'Jerry' from the 1920s who at just 5 feet, 7 inches tall is the shortest goalkeeper in the club's history?

593.   Name the former City boss who released a book entitled Life At The Kop.

594.   During a tour of the Far East in 1972 this Sky Blues centre-half won an arm wrestling contest with Mr Kim, the manager of the hotel the players were staying in, resulting in him buying the team free drinks all night. Name him.

595.   Prior to becoming a professional footballer what was Ray Graydon's occupation – carpenter, electrician or plumber?

596.   In what year was the Ricoh Arena opened?

597.   Can you name the former Aston Villa and England international who was Ron Atkinson's first signing as City boss?

598.   Name the Premier League side in season 2008/09 who were the first team to beat Coventry City at the Ricoh Arena.

599.   Can you name the 'United' who provided City's opposition when the club's record lowest League attendance was set on 24 April 1926, with just 1,660 fans turning up to watch the team play in a Third Division North game?

600.   He left the Sky Blues in 1938 after making 73 appearances for the club and scoring 29 goals. Name this player whose name is also the name of a Quentin Tarantino movie.

POT LUCK – 2

601. Name any one of the two 'Towns' that the Sky Blues have never met in a Football League, League Cup or FA Cup match.

602. Name two Premiership sides in season 2008/09 that the Sky Blues have met in the Premiership that begin and end with the same letter.

603. Can you name the former Coventry player who also managed the club and both played for and managed Leeds United, who was born on Christmas Day?

604. This Coventry City manager in 1956 guided Sweden to third place at the 1950 World Cup Finals in Brazil. Name him.

605. The fastest sending off in a FIFA World Cup Final match was 55 seconds between Uruguay and Scotland. Can you name the future City player and manager that was the victim of the foul?

606. Which City striker scored five goals for the Sky Blues in a 7-2 win over Chester City?

607. What future two-time European Cup winning manager turned down the opportunity of replacing Jimmy Hill as manager of City in October 1967?

608. Which European competition was Coventry not permitted to enter in season 1987/88?

609. Can you name the club that defeated Arsenal in the 1978 FA Cup final thereby depriving the Sky Blues of a place in the UEFA Cup for the following season?

610. Which future double European footballer of the year was rejected by City due to lack of height?

1970s

611.   Who was the Sky Blues manager during 1973/1974?

612.   Who were the two teams that Coventry beat both home and away during 1974/1975?

613.   Who was the club's highest League scorer with 14 goals in 37 starts and one substitute appearance?

614.   Who was the only player to play in all 42 League games for Coventry during 1970/1971?

615.   Against which Bulgarian club did John O'Rourke score a hat-trick in a 4-1 away win during September 1970 in the European Fairs Cup?

616.   In which position in Division One did the club finish during 1976/1977?

617.   True or false: West Bromwich Albion beat Coventry 7-1 away in Division One during October 1978?

618.   Who was Coventry's Player of the Year during 1978/1979?

619.   Who were the two players who got sent off for Coventry during 1971/1972, one away at Everton and the other at home to Liverpool?

620.   Which team did Coventry beat 4-1 away on the opening day of the 1975/1976 season with David Cross scoring a hat-trick?

ERNIE HUNT

621.   What is Ernie's real Christian name – Raymond, Richard or Roger?

622.   Name the hometown 'Town' where he began his professional career.

623.   Can you name the Midlands club Ernie joined in September 1965?

624.   In what year during the late 1960s did Ernie arrive at Highfield Road?

625.   From which Lancashire side did Ernie sign when he joined the Sky Blues.

626.   Following on from Q625 to the nearest £15,000 how much did City pay for his services?

627.   Can you name the 'Rovers' he went on loan to for a while from Coventry?

628.   How many seasons did Ernie spend at Highfield Road – five, six or seven?

629.   When Ernie left Highfield Road he joined this 'City'. Name them.

630.   In the summer of 1967 Ernie guested for a North American Soccer League team based in Los Angeles. This team's last name was the nickname of one of Ernie's clubs during his career. What were they called?

WHERE DID THEY GO – 2

*Match up the player with the team he joined
when he left Coventry City*

631.	Trevor Benjamin	Norwich City
632.	Andy Marriott	Walsall
633.	Barry Quinn	Perugia
634.	Scott Shearer	Leeds United
635.	Mo Konjic	Peterborough United
636.	Jay Boothroyd	Walsall
637.	Youssef Safri	Oxford United
638.	Steve Staunton	Bristol Rovers
639.	Julian Joachim	Colchester United
640.	Craig Pead	Derby County

TOMMY HUTCHISON

641.   At what Scottish 'Athletic' side did Tommy begin his professional playing career in 1965?

642.   Name the Lancashire club the legendary England centre forward, Stan Mortensen, signed Tommy for in February 1968.

643.   In what year during the early 1970s did he arrive at Highfield Road?

644.   Tommy won the Anglo-Italian Cup in 1971 with the club in Q642. Can you name his manager at the time, a man who went on to guide Sunderland to FA Cup glory in 1973?

645.   The Sky Blues paid £140,000 for Tommy and in addition to this fee City included this 'Billy' in the transfer. Name the player concerned.

646.   In what year did Tommy leave Highfield Road?

647.   Can you recall the 'City' he signed for when he left Coventry?

648.   Name the World Cup Finals where Tommy was a member of the Scotland squad.

649.   During his career Tommy both played for (1985 to 1991) and managed (1985 to 1986) this Welsh club. Can you name them?

650.   Name the two teams Tommy scored an FA Cup Final goal for during his career.

JIM BLYTH

651. At which famous Lancashire club, double winners in the 19th century, did Jim begin his professional career in 1971?

652. Following on from Q651 in what year did Jim arrive at Highfield Road?

653. Can you name the former European Cup winners he was set to join in 1979 in a £440,000 transfer but which failed to go through when he failed a medical on a suspect back?

654. To the nearest 25 how many League games did he play for the Sky Blues?

655. Can you recall the 'United' Jim went on loan to from City in 1975?

656. In what year during the early 1980s did he leave Highfield Road?

657. Name the Midlands team Jim joined when he left Coventry.

658. Which City manager did Jim serve as a coach to?

659. Can you name the young goalkeeper who Jim was responsible for bringing to City and who later broke the British transfer fee for a goalkeeper (£6 million) when Liverpool signed him in August 2001?

660. In season 2008/09 Jim was the goalkeeping coach at this Scottish club and a mentor to Artur Boruc, the Polish international goalkeeper. Name the team.

POT LUCK – 3

661.   Name the Republic of Ireland international who is the youngest Sky Blue to be capped by his country, aged 17 years and 200 days v Austria on 30 May 1971.

662.   Which 'Wanderers' did City record their highest win over on Christmas Day?

663.   Who was the first Coventry City player to have received a red card during a FIFA World Cup game, playing for an African nation?

664.   Which goalkeeper, who had two spells at Highfield Road from 1937 to 1951 and 1956 to 1958, holds the record for the oldest player to pull on the Sky Blue shirt?

665.   Can you name the former British Prime Minister who had a trophy named in his honour after his death on 24 January 1965 by the chairman of the Sky Blues, Derrick Robins?

666.   Following on from the previous question, name any one of the two London sides that City played in the competition.

667.   Name the former Coventry City player who served in the Bosnian army.

668.   How many current/former Coventry players at the time had lost their lives during World War II – 1, 11 or 21?

669.   Who is the only Sky Blues player to have managed the Welsh national side twice?

670.   Can you name the Coventry player who in 1959 played for the club and served with the RAF at Bridgnorth?

DAVE CLEMENTS

671.   At what Irish League club did Dave begin his playing career – Glentoran, Linfield or Portadown?

672.   Can you name the Midlands club which signed Dave in 1963 from the team in Q671 but where Dave failed to make it into the first team?

673.   Which City manager brought Dave to Highfield Road in 1964?

674.   Dave scored on his debut for the Sky Blues against this side whose name both begins and ends with the letter 'N'. Name them.

675.   How many seasons did Dave spend with the Sky Blues – five, seven or nine?

676.   To the nearest 25 how many games did he play for Coventry City?

677.   When he left City, Dave signed for a Yorkshire club. Can you name them?

678.   Which Lancashire club did he sign for in 1973 remaining there until 1976?

679.   During his career Dave played for the same team as the legendary Pele and Franz Beckenbauer. Can you name the team?

680.   What team (excluding NASL sides) did Dave both play for and manage during his career?

IAN WALLACE

681.   In which Scottish city was Ian born – Dundee, Edinburgh or Glasgow?

682.   Name the Scottish club nicknamed 'The Sons' where Ian began his playing career in 1974.

683.   In what year during the mid-1970s did Ian arrive at Highfield Road?

684.   To the nearest £15,000 how much did the Sky Blues pay for his services?

685.   Can you recall the City manager who signed him for the club?

686.   When he arrived at Highfield Road who was his main strike partner in the City side?

687.   Can you name the reigning European Cup holders who paid City £1.25 million for Ian's services in 1980?

688.   Ian won three full Scottish caps during his career, how many goals did he score in these three games?

689.   Name the North East club he played 34 League games for, scoring six times from 1984 to 1986.

690.   Despite being a prolific goal scorer he won only three caps for Scotland. When Ian scored his only international goal for his country versus Bulgaria in February 1978 his Coventry team-mate was in goal. Name him.

THE BIRMINGHAM CITY CONNECTION - 1

All you have to do here is associate the player who left Coventry City to join Birmingham City with the years he played for the Sky Blues

691.	Peter Ndlovu	1922-27
692.	Tommy Briggs	1989-92
693.	Fred Hawley	1995-2000
694.	Gerry Daly	1950-54
695.	Kevin Drinkell	1988-89
696.	David Smith	1991-97
697.	Tony Hateley	1980-84
698.	David Burrows	1919-20
699.	Jackie Randle	1988-93
700.	Bill Bradbury	1950-51

HONOURS

Match up the honour with the year the club achieved it

701.	FA Cup Winners	1968
702.	Division Three (South) Champions	1967
703.	FA Youth Cup Runners-up	1936
704.	Division Four Runners-up	2000
705.	FA Youth Cup Runners-up	1964
706.	Division Two Champions	1970
707.	FA Youth Cup Winners	1987
708.	FA Youth Cup Runners-up	1999
709.	Division Three Champions	1987
710.	FA Youth Cup Runners-up	1959

GARY BREEN

711. At which London club did Gary begin his career as a Youth Team player but never made a senior appearance for the side?

712. Name the non-League 'United' Gary joined in 1991 making his debut for them aged 17.

713. Can you name the Kent club he signed for in 1992?

714. Following on from Q713 name the 'United' he signed for after he left this club.

715. To the nearest £500,000 how much did the Sky Blues pay for his services?

716. What London club did Gary join when he left Highfield Road?

717. During his career Gary scored more League goals for this North East club than any other. Who are they?

718. Following on from Q717 can you name the club he signed for in 2006 thereby reuniting him with his old boss?

719. Name the manager who managed Gary at the teams in Q717 and 718 and at international level.

720. How many international caps did he win with the Republic of Ireland – 63, 73 or 83?

RICHARD SHAW

721. In which position did Richard play during his playing days – defender, midfielder or striker?

722. How many League goals did Richard score for the Sky Blues in his career?

723. Which London club did Richard sign for when he left Coventry in 2006?

724. In which year was Richard born – 1966, 1967 or 1968?

725. At which London club did Richard start his football career, also signing from them to join Coventry in 1995?

726. Can you name the two seasons Richard won the Player of the Year award at Coventry?

727. Which Sky Blues manager signed Richard for Coventry City in 1995?

728. True or false: Richard played in the 1990 FA Cup final?

729. In how many of Coventry's 38 Premier League matches did Richard play in?

730. During 1989, at which club did Richard play four matches whilst on loan from his first professional club?

731. *If the Sky Blues visited Stamford Bridge, what team would they be playing away?*

732. *If the Sky Blues visited Pride Park Stadium, what team would they be playing away?*

733. *If the Sky Blues visited Saltergate, what team would they be playing away?*

734. *If the Sky Blues visited Deva Stadium, what 'City' would they be playing away?*

735. *If the Sky Blues visited Broadfield Stadium, what 'Town' would they be playing away?*

736. *If the Sky Blues visited the Fraser Eagle Stadium, what team would they be playing away?*

737. *If the Sky Blues visited The Lawn, what team would they be playing away?*

738. *If the Sky Blues visited Turf Moor, what team would they be playing away?*

739. *If the Sky Blues visited The Weston Community Stadium, what 'United' would they be playing away?*

740. *If the Sky Blues visited Victoria Road, what double-barrelled team would they be playing away?*

741. If the Sky Blues were in opposition against the Imps, what 'City' would they be playing?

742. If the Sky Blues were in opposition against the Reds, what former English two-times European Cup winners would they be playing?

743. If the Sky Blues were in opposition against the Rams, who would they be playing?

744. If the Sky Blues were in opposition against the Vikings, what 'Rovers' would they be playing?

745. If the Sky Blues were in opposition against the Terriers, what 'Town' would they be playing?

746. If the Sky Blues were in opposition against the Eagles, who would they be playing?

747. If the Sky Blues were in opposition against the Tractor Boys, who would they be playing?

748. If the Sky Blues were in opposition against the Monkey Hangers, who would they be playing?

749. If the Sky Blues were in opposition against the Silkmen, what 'Town' would they be playing?

750. If the Sky Blues were in opposition against the Fleet, who would they be playing?

WHICH POSITION – 1

*Match up the player with the position they
played for Coventry City*

751.	Peter Atherton	Goalkeeper
752.	Chris Kirkland	Defender
753.	Danny Thomas	Striker
754.	Noel Whelan	Defender
755.	Cyrille Regis	Defender
756.	Colin Hawkins	Striker
757.	Richard Shaw	Striker
758.	Mark Hateley	Defender
759.	Bill Glazier	Defender
760.	Willie Boland	Goalkeeper

WHERE DID THEY COME FROM – 3

Match up the player with his previous club,
before joining Coventry City

761.	Darren Huckerby	**Hartlepool United**
762.	Lee Hughes	**Seville**
763.	Laurent Delorge	**Luton Town**
764.	Dimitrios Konstantopoulos	**Aberdeen**
765.	Regis Genaux	**West Bromwich Albion**
766.	Ranar Normann	**Manchester United**
767.	Paul Telfer	**Liège**
768.	Dion Dublin	**Newcastle United**
769.	Robert Jarni	**Ghent**
770.	Eion Jess	**Lillestrom**

MIXED BAG – 3

771. Highfield Road was pencilled in by the FA to stage a second replay of the 1970 FA Cup Final should the first replay end in a draw. Name either one of the two sides involved in the 1970 FA Cup Final.

772. Can you name the former Aberdeen player and European Cup Winners' Cup winner who Gary McAllister appointed as his assistant manager at City in the summer of 2002?

773. He joined Southampton in 1950 and was their top goal scorer for two consecutive years before joining City in 1952. In season 1954/55 he left Highfield Road and joined Birmingham City after 89 games and an impressive haul of 51 goals for the Sky Blues. Who is he?

774. Name the former City boss who released a book entitled Everton Winter, Mexican Summer.

775. Who in season 1954/55 became the first caretaker/manager of the club?

776. To the nearest £25 million how much did it cost to build the Ricoh Arena?

777. What caused the Coventry City versus Sheffield United match at Highfield Road in March 1972 to be abandoned?

778. Can you name the 'Don' who scored a hat-trick in consecutive games for City against Crystal Palace on 29 November 1952 and versus Torquay United on 13 December 1952?

779. Name the 'David' who signed for the Sky Blues from Birmingham City in 1993, making 96 appearances for the club and scoring three goals before leaving Highfield Road in 1996.

780. This former Coventry City star was rejected by Bolton Wanderers at the same time as the future England World Cup winner. Name the 'Ernie' concerned.

AWAY DAYS – 5

781. If the Sky Blues visited Craven Cottage, what team would they be playing away?

782. If the Sky Blues visited Portman Road, what 'Town' would they be playing away?

783. If the Sky Blues visited Belle Vue, what 'Rovers' would they be playing away?

784. If the Sky Blues visited Blundell Park, what 'Town' would they be playing away?

785. If the Sky Blues visited St James's Park, what team named 'City' would they be playing away?

786. If the Sky Blues visited the Reebok Stadium, what team would they be playing away?

787. If the Sky Blues visited Elland Road, what team would they be playing away?

788. If the Sky Blues visited Priestfield Stadium, what team would they be playing away?

789. If the Sky Blues visited Brisbane Road, what team would they be playing away?

790. If the Sky Blues visited The Williamson Motors Stadium, what team would they be playing away?

WHERE DID THEY GO – 3

Match up the player with the team he joined
when he left Coventry City

791.	Dele Adebola	Brighton & Hove Albion
792.	Robert Page	Mansfield Town
793.	Gary McSheffrey	Bristol City
794.	Colin Cameron	Walsall
795.	Stephen Hughes	Crystal Palace
796.	Andrew Whing	Huddersfield Town
797.	Andy Morrell	Crewe Alexandra
798.	Ryan Lynch	Birmingham City
799.	Kevin Pressman	MK Dons
800.	James Scowcroft	Blackpool

PLAYER OF THE YEAR

Match up the player with the year he won the Player of the Year award at Coventry City

801.	1972/1973	Kevin Gallacher
802.	1974/1975	Nicky Platnauer
803.	1975/1976	Peter Atherton
804.	1979/1980	Brian Borrows
805.	1983/1984	Gary Gillespie
806.	1986/1987	Gary McAllister
807.	1990/1991	Tommy Hutchison
808.	1992/1993	Graham Oakey
809.	1994/1995	Willie Carr
810.	1999/2000	Steve Ogrizovic

WHO ARE WE PLAYING? – 5

811.   If the Sky Blues were in opposition against the Red Devils, who would they be playing?

812.   If the Sky Blues were in opposition against the Hatters, which 'Town' would they be playing?

813.   If the Sky Blues were in opposition against the Grecians, which 'City' would they be playing?

814.   If the Sky Blues were in opposition against the 'O's, who would they be playing?

815.   If the Sky Blues were in opposition against the Grays, which 'Athletic' would they be playing?

816.   If the Sky Blues were in opposition against Pompey, who would they be playing?

817.   If the Sky Blues were in opposition against the Lions, who would they be playing?

818.   If the Sky Blues were in opposition against the Quakers, who would they be playing?

819.   If the Sky Blues were in opposition against the Cobblers, who would they be playing?

820.   If the Sky Blues were in opposition against the Shaymen, which 'Town' would they be playing?

WHICH POSITION – 2

Match up the player with the position they played for Coventry City

821.	Bryan King	Striker
822.	Ellery Cairo	Goalkeeper
823.	Gary Breen	Midfielder
824.	Steve Whitton	Goalkeeper
825.	Michael Hughes	Defender
826.	Colin Hendry	Midfielder
827.	Steve Sedgley	Defender
828.	Les Sealey	Midfielder
829.	Trevor Peake	Striker
830.	John Hartson	Midfielder

CYRILLE REGIS

831. In which year did Cyrille join Coventry City from West Bromwich Albion?

832. Against which team did Cyrille score Coventry's 90th minute equaliser in the 1-1 home draw during New Year's Day 1985?

833. What was the score when Cyrille made his Coventry City League debut at home to Newcastle United?

834. In which position did Cyrille play during his playing days?

835. How many full international caps did Cyrille pick up for England in his career?

836. What was Cyrille's best tally in a League season, during 1986/1987 – 12 goals, 14 goals or 16 goals?

837. What award was Cyrille given by the Queen in 2008?

838. Against which club did Cyrille score his first League goal of the 1988/1989 season during a 2-1 away win during September 1988?

839. How many League goals did Cyrille score during his Coventry City career – 47, 57 or 67?

840. Which two Midlands teams did Cyrille play for after he left Coventry City?

THE BIRMINGHAM CITY
CONNECTION – 2

All you have to do here is associate the player who left Birmingham City to join Coventry City with the years he played for the Sky Blues

841.	David Rennie	**1996-97**
842.	John Gayle	**1947-50**
843.	Frank Croweq	**1954-55**
844.	Fred Gardner	**1920-22**
845.	Gary Breen	**1945-49**
846.	Don Dearson	**1995**
847.	William Morgan	**1993-96**
848.	Ken Rowley	**1993-94**
849.	Liam Daish	**1997-2002**
850.	Chris Whyte	**1919-20**

1992/1993 – FIRST PREMIER LEAGUE SEASON

851. Who was Coventry's manager during this season?

852. Which two goalkeepers did Coventry use to play their 42 League matches?

853. Who was the club's highest League scorer with 17 goals?

854. Who was the club's Player of the Year?

855. True or false: Coventry won their first four Premier League away games?

856. Which London club did Coventry beat both home and away during this season?

857. In which position did the club finish in the Premier League?

858. Can you name the Coventry player who scored the club's first ever Premier League goal on his debut after just nine minutes against Middlesbrough during August 1992?

859. Can you recall the score when Coventry played Liverpool at High Road during this season – 3-1, 4-1 or 5-1?

860. Can you name the three goalscorers who scored against Leeds United on the last day of the season, in a 3-3 draw?

HARRY BARRATT

861. What south coast club did Harry's father Joe play for?

862. On what highly significant day of the year was Harry born?

863. In which year during the early 1930s did the young Harry sign for City?

864. Can you name the non-League 'Town' Harry was sent on loan to by the Sky Blues?

865. Name the 'Rovers' he made his Coventry debut against in April 1938.

866. Harry played in every position for City except one. Which one?

867. What position did Harry take up at Highfield Road in the summer of 1955 when Jesse Carver was manager?

868. Can you name the Kent-based club who appointed Harry as their manager in 1964?

869. To the nearest 25 how many appearances did Harry make for the Sky Blues?

870. Following on from Q869 how many goals did he score in those games – 12, 16 or 20?

TREVOR PEAKE

871. Can you name the non-League club nicknamed 'Boro' where Trevor began his playing career in 1978?

872. In which year during the early 1980s did he arrive at Highfield Road as a player?

873. From which 'City' did the Sky Blues sign Trevor?

874. In which year during the early 1990s did Trevor leave City?

875. Following on from Q874 can you name the 'Town' he signed for?

876. In which year did Trevor finally hang-up his boots as a player – 1996, 1998 or 2000?

877. Following on from Q876 name the Sky Blues boss who brought Trevor back to the club to coach the Under-19 side shortly after he retired from playing.

878. Can you name the year he was made manager of Coventry City?

879. Who did Trevor succeed as boss of the Sky Blues?

880. Following on from Q879 which former Coventry player co-managed the team with Trevor?

BOBBY GOULD

881. How many managerial spells has Bobby had at Coventry City?

882. In which position did Bobby play during his playing days?

883. What is Bobby's middle name?

884. In which year did Bobby leave Highfield Road as a player?

885. Following on from the previous question, which London team did Bobby sign for when he left Coventry City?

886. Which manager handed Bobby his Coventry City debut?

887. Against which team did Bobby score a brace in the 3-3 League draw during August 1967?

888. In which position did Bobby guide Coventry to during 1992/1993?

889. Which manager took over from Bobby when he left Highfield Road as manager in 1993?

890. Which country did Bobby manage between 1995 and 1999?

MICK QUINN

891.   Which Sky Blues manager signed Mick on loan from
       Newcastle United in November 1992?

892.   Against which team did Mick score twice on his
       Coventry League debut in a 3-2 home defeat?

893.   At which London club did Mick score his first hat-trick
       for Coventry City during 14 August 1993 in a 3-0 away
       win?

894.   Where was Mick born in 1962?

895.   Which club did Mick play for between 1983 and 1985?

896.   Mick scored 17 League goals in his first season at
       Coventry City, how many League games did he start –
       24, 26 or 28?

897.   What was the name of Mick's autobiography?

898.   Against which team did Mick score a brace for
       Coventry during November 1993 in a 2-1 home win?

899.   True or false: Mick won the Player of the Year award in
       his first season at Highfield Road?

900.   How many League goals did Mick score for the Sky
       Blues during 1993/1994 – six, seven or eight?

MIXED BAG – 4

901. Name the 'George' who Harry Barratt saw play for Snowdown Colliery whom he recommended to the City board and was signed by the club on Harry's recommendation.

902. Can you name the 'Jim' who left Highfield Road in 1982 after 10 years with the Sky Blues to join Birmingham City?

903. To the nearest 10,000 what is the highest attendance for any Coventry City FA Cup game?

904. Name the Coventry City manager who was the first to be named Premier League Manager of the Month.

905. Can you name the Danish-born Sky Blue who was the first player to score a League goal at the Ricoh Arena?

906. Following on from the question above, although he was born in Denmark what country did he represent at international level winning 10 caps and scoring one goal?

907. In season 2008-09, what was the Ricoh Arena's maximum capacity – 32,000 or 34,000 or 36,000?

908. In January 2005 the Sky Blues witnessed their lowest ever attendance (7,629) for a home FA Cup tie (excluding qualifying rounds). What team with an 'x' in their name did City's fans see beaten 3-0 in the FA Cup Third Round at Highfield Road?

909. Name the former Manchester United captain and Sky Blues boss who released a book entitled United We Stand.

910. This former Everton player was made caretaker manager of Coventry City in 2005 for three games. Who is he?

POSITIONS IN THE LEAGUE – 3

Match the season with the position Coventry City finished in the League

911.	1967/1968	14th in the Premier League
912.	1969/1970	16th in the Premier League
913.	1978/1979	19th in the Championship
914.	1981/1982	15th in the Premier League
915.	1985/1986	12th in Division One
916.	1989/1990	14th in Division One
917.	1994/1995	18th in Division One
918.	1998/1999	10th in Division One
919.	1999/2000	20th in Division One
920.	2004/2005	6th in Division One

CONSECUTIVE SCORERS

*Match the player with the goals he scored
in consecutive games*

921. Mick Quinn   4 goals in 3
                                games (2008)

922. Dave Clements   19 goals in 10
                                games (1931)

923. Andy Morrell   3 goals in 2
                                games (2000)

924. Bobby Gould   4 goals in 2
                                games (1999)

925. Terry Bly   9 goals in 6
                                games (1992)

926. Clarrie Bourton   4 goals in 3
                                games (2005)

927. Darren Huckerby   5 goals in 5
                                games (1965)

928. Elliott Ward   9 goals in 7
                                games (1962)

929. Stern John   5 goals in 5
                                games (2003)

930. Cedric Roussel   6 goals in 6
                                games (1967)

GORDON STRACHAN

931.   In which year did Gordon sign for Coventry from
       Leeds United?

932.   What is Gordon's nationality?

933.   How many goals did Gordon score in his 50
       international caps?

934.   In what position did Gordon play during his playing
       days – defender, midfielder or striker?

935.   True or false: when Gordon took the manager's job at
       Highfield Road in the 1990s it was his first
       managerial appointment of his career?

936.   How old was Gordon when he made his last Coventry
       City appearance as a player?

937.   In which position did Gordon guide Coventry to during
       1998/1999 in the Premier League?

938.   Who did Gordon take over from as Coventry manager
       during November 1996?

939.   True or false: Gordon scored three League goals in his
       Coventry City career?

940.   Which team did Gordon manage from 2001 to 2004?

WILLIE CARR

941. In which Scottish city was Willie born?

942. Can you recall the year during the late 1960s in which Willie joined Coventry City?

943. What name was given to a famous goal which Willie was involved in during a First Division match shown on Match of the Day in October 1970?

944. Following on from Q943 against which Lancashire team did Willie take a free kick by gripping the ball between his ankles and flicking it up for a team-mate to volley into the net?

945. Can you recall the scorer of this goal which won the 1970/71 Goal of the Season award?

946. Against which London club did Willie make his debut for the Sky Blues?

947. In what year during the mid-1970s did he leave Coventry City?

948. When Willie left Highfield Road he joined another Midlands club. Name them.

949. What winners' medal did Willie collect with the team in Q948 in season 1979/80?

950. Name the London club where he ended his professional playing career in 1983.

LOAN PLAYERS

Match up the player to the club he signed on loan from

951.	Ian Bennett	*Leicester City*
952.	Luke Steele	*Liverpool*
953.	Johnnie Jackson	*Blackburn Rovers*
954.	Lee Sawyer	*Sunderland*
955.	Paul Trollope	*Birmingham City*
956.	Tim Flowers	*Tottenham Hotspur*
957.	Jordan Henderson	*Manchester City*
958.	Matt Jansen	*Chelsea*
959.	Kasper Schmeichel	*Fulham*
960.	Richie Partridge	*Manchester United*

GARRY THOMPSON

961. Which position did Garry play during his playing days?

962. Which team did Garry join when he left Highfield Road in 1983?

963. Which manager gave Garry his Coventry debut?

964. What is Garry's middle name?

965. How many League goals did Garry score for the Sky Blues during 1981/1982 in his 35 starts and one substitute appearance?

966. Against which team did Garry score the only goal during September 1982 in a 1-0 home League win?

967. Against which team did Garry score a brace in a 4-0 home League win during September 1981?

968. Against which team did Garry score the winning goal during November 1978 in a 2-1 home League win?

969. How many League goals did Garry score in his first season at Coventry City in his five starts and one substitute appearance?

970. In which year was Garry born in Birmingham – 1959, 1960 or 1961?

DION DUBLIN

971.   Against which team did Dion make his Coventry League debut in a 2-2 away draw?

972.   True or false: Dion scored in his first four League games for the Sky Blues?

973.   In which year did Dion sign for Coventry City?

974.   How many League goals did Dion score in his first season, having played in 31 League matches?

975.   How many full England caps did Dion win during his football career – 4, 14 or 40?

976.   Can you name the two seasons that Dion won the Player of the Year award whilst a Coventry City player?

977.   For which club did Dion play between 2004 and 2006?

978.   Against which team did Dion score a hat-trick for the Sky Blues in a 4-3 away defeat during December 1995?

979.   Against which club did Dion score in his final League match for Coventry during November 1998 in a 2-1 away defeat?

980.   Which Midlands team did Dion join when he left Highfield Road?

SKY BLUE AUTHORS

All you have to do here is associate the manager/player with the book he wrote

981.	Ron Atkinson	**Attack From The Back**
982.	George Raynor	**Crown Green Bowls: The Rules Of The Game**
983.	Jimmy Hill	**Who Ate All The Pies?**
984.	Harry Barratt	**Hard Man, Hard Knocks**
985.	Mark Hateley	**A Different Ball Game**
986.	Gary McAllister	**Football Crazy**
987.	Phil Neal	**The Great Ones**
988.	Terry Yorath	**Captain's Log**
989.	Joe Mercer	**Top Mark**
990.	Mick Quinn	**Football Ambassador At Large**

GORDON MILNE

991. Which famous Lancashire side did both Gordon and his father Jimmy play for?

992. Can you name the Lancashire side Gordon joined in 1960 after leaving the team in Q991?

993. Following on from Q992 name the legendary manager of this team, famous for his quotes, who signed Gordon for the team.

994. What seaside club did Gordon sign for in 1967?

995. This 'Athletic' side appointed Gordon as their player/manager in 1970. Who are they?

996. In what year during the early 1970s did Gordon arrive at Highfield as team manager but did not assume overall control of team affairs?

997. Following on from Q996 can you name the Coventry City boss he joined at Highfield Road?

998. In what year did Gordon take overall charge of the team?

999. What 'City' did he become the manager of when he left Coventry?

1000. Can you name the Turkish club which appointed Gordon their manager in 1987 and guided them to three Turkish League Championships in 1990, 1991 and 1992?

ANSWERS

HISTORY OF THE CLUB

1. The Sky Blues
2. 1898
3. Ben Mackey
4. 1899
5. Queens Park Rangers
6. Ray Ranson
7. 1970/1971
8. Chelsea (Coventry City lost 2-0 in the FA Cup quarter-final)
9. Everton
10. 1919

NATIONALITIES

11.	John Aloisi	Australia
12.	Cedric Roussel	Belgium
13.	Michael Mifsud	Malta
14.	Peter Ndlovu	Zimbabwe
15.	Marques Isaias	Brazil
16.	Bjarni Gudjonsson	Iceland
17.	Martin Jol	Holland
18.	Youssef Safri	Morocco
19.	Ysrael Zuniga	Peru
20.	Wayne Andrews	Barbados

GARY McALLISTER

21. Nottingham Forest
22. Five
23. Ron Atkinson
24. West Ham United
25. Six
26. 2002

27.   Midfielder

28.   Blackpool

29.   Leeds United

30.   Wimbledon (away), Sheffield Wednesday (away),
      Middlesbrough (home)

SQUAD NUMBERS – 2008/2009

31.	Marcus Hall	3
32.	Guillaume Beuzelin	7
33.	Clinton Morrison	19
34.	Michael Doyle	8
35.	Leon McKenzie	14
36.	Scott Dann	6
37.	Ben Turner	20
38.	Keiren Westwood	1
39.	Daniel Fox	4
40.	Julian Gray	11

WHERE DID THEY COME FROM - 1

41.	Freddy Eastwood	Wolves
42.	Scott Dann	Walsall
43.	Michael Hughes	Crystal Palace
44.	Guillaume Beuzelin	Hibernian
45.	Clinton Morrison	Crystal Palace
46.	Kevin Kyle	Sunderland
47.	Julian Gray	Birmingham City
48.	Stephen Wright	Sunderland
49.	Dennis Wise	Southampton
50.	Andy Marshall	Millwall

STEVE OGRIZOVIC

51. Shrewsbury Town
52. FA Cup winners' medal
53. Aston Villa
54. Liverpool
55. True
56. 1986/1987
57. Sheffield Wednesday
58. Bobby Gould
59. English
60. Sheffield Wednesday

MANAGERS

61.	Ron Atkinson	1995/1996
62.	Gordon Strachan	1999/2000
63.	John Sillett	1989/1990
64.	George Curtis	1986/1987
65.	Dave Sexton	1982/1983
66.	Gordon Strachan	2000/2001
67.	Noel Cantwell	1970/1971
68.	Bobby Gould	1983/1984
69.	Gordon Milne	1979/1980
70.	Gordon Milne	1978/1979

TERRY BUTCHER

71. 77
72. John Poynton
73. Liverpool
74. Tottenham Hotspur
75. Paul Furlong
76. Six

77.	Glasgow Rangers
78.	George Burley
79.	Ipswich Town
80.	Don Howe

INTERNATIONALS

81.	Roy Wegerle	41 Caps for USA
82.	Tom Hutchison	17 Caps for Scotland
83.	Steve Staunton	102 Caps for Republic of Ireland
84.	Terry Yorath	59 Caps for Wales
85.	Peter Ndlovu	100 Caps for Zimbabwe
86.	Phil Babb	35 Caps for Republic of Ireland
87.	Ronnie Rees	39 Caps for Wales
88.	Liam Daish	5 Caps for Republic of Ireland
89.	Gary McAllister	57 Caps for Scotland
90.	Gerry Daly	48 Caps for Republic of Ireland

LEAGUE APPEARANCES - 1

91.	Steve Ogrizovic	504
92.	Dave Bennett	172
93.	Dion Dublin	145
94.	Robbie Keane	31
95.	John Hartson	12
96.	Keith Houchen	54
97.	Steve Staunton	70
98.	Brain Kilcline	173
99.	Willie Carr	252
100.	Cyrille Regis	238

THE LEAGUE CUP

| 101. | Manchester United |

102.   *Semi-Final*

103.   *Nottingham Forest*

104.   *Newcastle United*

105.   *Sunderland*

106.   *Manchester City*

107.   *Tottenham Hotspur*

108.   *West Ham United*

109.   *Barrow*

110.   *Portsmouth*

AWAY DAYS – 1

111.   *Manchester City*

112.   *Leicester City*

113.   *Hartlepool United*

114.   *Lincoln City*

115.   *Gravesend & Northfleet*

116.   *Sunderland*

117.   *Luton Town*

118.   *Huddersfield Town*

119.   *Macclesfield Town*

120.   *Halifax Town*

WHO ARE WE PLAYING? – 1

121.   *Arsenal*

122.   *Brighton & Hove Albion*

123.   *Barnsley*

124.   *Barnet or Brentford*

125.   *Accrington Stanley*

126.   *Aston Villa*

127.   *Burnley*

128.   *Blackpool*

129.	**Bristol Rovers**

130.	**Burton Albion**

POSITIONS IN THE LEAGUE - 1

131.	1970/1971	10th in Division One
132.	1975/1976	14th in Division One
133.	1982/1983	19th in Division One
134.	1986/1987	10th in Division One
135.	1988/1989	7th in Division One
136.	1990/1991	16th in Division One
137.	1992/1993	15th in the Premier League
138.	1996/1997	16th in the Premier League
139.	2005/2006	8th in the Championship
140.	2007/2008	21st in the Championship

2008/2009

141.	**Norwich City**

142.	**Elliott Ward**

143.	**Bristol City**

144.	**Aldershot Town**

145.	**Swansea City**

146.	**Blackburn Rovers**

147.	**17th**

148.	**Blackpool**

149.	**Clinton Morrison**

150.	**Chelsea**

FA CUP WINNERS – 1987 – 1

151.	**George Curtis**

152.	**Tottenham Hotspur**

153.	**3-2**

154. *Dave Bennett*

155. *Steve Ogrizovic*

156. *True*

157. *Gary Mabbutt*

158. *Leeds United*

159. *Sheffield Wednesday*

160. *Manchester United*

BIG WINS

161.	*v. Trowbridge (away),*	
	FA Cup, November 1963	**6-1**
162.	*v. Queens Park Rangers (away),*	
	League, November 1963	**6-3**
163.	*v. Bolton Wanderers (away),*	
	League, January 1998	**5-1**
164.	*v. Bristol City (home),*	
	League, April 1934	**9-0**
165.	*v. Rotherham United (home),*	
	League, November 1925	**7-1**
166.	*v. Rushden & Diamonds (home),*	
	League Cup, October 2002	**8-0**
167.	*v. Scunthorpe United (home),*	
	FA Cup, December 1954	**4-0**
168.	*v. Wolves (home),*	
	League, December 1922	**7-1**
169.	*v. Torquay United (home),*	
	League, December 1952	**7-2**
170.	*v. Lincoln City (away),*	
	FA Cup, March 1963	**5-1**

1999/2000

171. Gordon Strachan
172. Derby County
173. Robbie Keane
174. Youssef Chippo and Mustapha Hadji
175. Gary McAllister
176. 14th
177. Arsenal
178. Manchester United
179. False
180. Gary McAllister

WHO AM I?

181. Micky Adams
182. Kevin Gallacher
183. Kenny Sansom
184. Lee Carsley
185. Kenny Hibbitt
186. Nii Lamptey
187. Roland Nilsson
188. Kevin MacDonald
189. Carlton Palmer
190. David Busst

ROLAND NILSSON

191. 1997
192. Gordon Strachan
193. Manchester United (Lost 3-0)
194. 1999
195. Helsingborgs IF
196. 2001/02

197.   69

198.   Three

199.   IFK Göteborg

200.   Malmö FF

FA CUP WINNERS – 1987 – 2

201.   Keith Houchen

202.   Brian Kilcline

203.   Graham Rodger

204.   David Phillips

205.   2-2

206.   Osvoldo Ardiles

207.   Hillsborough (Sheffield)

208.   Clive Allen

209.   Dave Bennett

210.   Seven

MATCH THE YEAR - 1

211.	Magnus Hedman signed for Coventry City	1997
212.	Coventry played their first League match at Highfield Road	1919
213.	Robbie Keane leaves the Sky Blues for Inter Milan	2000
214.	Ray Pointer scored on his Coventry debut	1965
215.	Roland Nilsson was appointed as Coventry manager	2001
216.	Terry Gibson scored on his Sky Blues debut	1983
217.	Peugeot became the clubs sponsors	1989
218.	Peter Ndlovu left Highfield Road for Birmingham City	1997
219.	Robert Jarni signed for Coventry	1998

1980s

221.   **Watford**

222.   **Gordon Milne**

223.   **Middlesbrough**

224.   **1981**

225.   **Watford (4th round, 1-0)**

226.   **Jimmy Hill**

227.   **Dave Sexton**

228.   **Derby County**

229.   **John Sillett**

230.   **Sutton United**

2000/2001

231.   **Leicester City**

232.   **Gordon Strachan**

233.   **19th**

234.   **28**

235.   **Gary Breen**

236.   **Craig Bellamy, Moustapha Hadji and John Hartson**

237.   **Everton**

238.   **False: they lost 3-1 to Middlesbrough on the opening day of the season**

239.   **Craig Bellamy and Cedric Roussel**

240.   **Eight**

MICKEY GYNN

241.   **1961**

242.   **Midfielder**

243.   **Peterborough United**

244. **Bobby Gould**

245. **Watford**

246. **Two**

247. **Manchester United**

248. **Stoke City**

249. **Liverpool**

250. **Two**

FRANK AUSTIN

251. **1933**

252. **Torquay United**

253. **Harry Storer**

254. **Full-back**

255. **Two**

256. **False**

257. **John**

258. **England**

259. **Jimmy Hill**

260. **302**

GEORGE CURTIS

261. **Don Mackay**

262. **1955**

263. **John Sillett**

264. **Aston Villa**

265. **Third Division Championship Winners' Medal**

266. **West Ham United**

267. **False**

268. **Southampton**

269. **Snowdown WC**

270. **Steve Ogrizovic**

DIVISION TWO CHAMPTION – 1966/1967

271.   Hull City

272.   Wolverhampton Wanderers

273.   One point

274.   Jimmy Hill

275.   25

276.   Ipswich Town

277.   Bill Glazier

278.   Carlisle United

279.   Noel Cantwell

280.   Millwall

TERRY GIBSON

281.   Tottenham Hotspur

282.   Striker

283.   Bradley

284.   Watford

285.   17

286.   True

287.   Stoke City

288.   11

289.   Manchester United

290.   Wimbledon

WHERE DID THEY GO - 1

291.	Cedric Roussel	Wolves
292.	Trond-Egil Soltvedt	Southampton
293.	Gary McAllister	Liverpool
294.	Brian Borrows	Swindon Town
295.	Colin Hendry	Bolton Wanderers
296.	Noel Whelan	Middlesbrough

297.	Willie Boland	Cardiff City
298.	John Salako	Bolton Wanderers
299.	Robbie Keane	Inter Milan
300.	Cyrille Regis	Aston Villa

AWAY DAYS – 2

301	Birmingham City
302	Cardiff City
303	Northampton Town
304	Bristol Rovers
305	Altrincham
306	Blackburn Rovers
307	West Bromwich Albion
308	Cambridge United
309	Bury
310	Burton Albion

WHO ARE WE PLAYING? – 2

311.	Plymouth Argyle
312.	Cardiff City
313.	AFC Bournemouth
314.	Carlisle United
315.	Aldershot Town
316.	Charlton Athletic
317.	West Bromwich Albion
318.	Bradford City
319.	Chester City
320.	Cambridge United

DIVISION THREE CHAMPIONS – 1963/1964

| 321. | Crystal Palace |

322. *True*

323. *22*

324. *Notts County*

325. *Jimmy Hill*

326. *Colchester United (at Highfield Road)*

327. *Trowbridge Town*

328. *Southend United*

329. *Hull City*

330. *Bristol Rovers*

WHERE DID THEY COME FROM - 2

331.	*Kirk Stephens*	*Luton Town*
332.	*Jim Melrose*	*Leicester City*
333.	*Brian Borrows*	*Bolton Wanderers*
334.	*Leon McKenzie*	*Norwich City*
335.	*Peter Barnes*	*West Bromwich Albion*
336.	*John Williams*	*Swansea City*
337.	*Michael Doyle*	*Celtic*
338.	*Peter Atherton*	*Wigan Athletic*
339.	*Sandy Robertson*	*Rangers*
340.	*David Burrows*	*Everton*

NICKNAMES - 1

341.	*Robert Turner*	*Leggy*
342.	*Ernie Toseland*	*Twinkletoes*
343.	*Steve Mokone*	*Kalamazoo*
344.	*George Curtis*	*Iron Man*
345.	*Chris Cattlin*	*Spider*
346.	*Ysrael Zuniga*	*Cachete (Big Cheeks)*
347.	*Mick Quinn*	*Sumo*
348.	*Noel Whelan*	*Snowy*

| 349. | Brian Kilcline | Killer |
| 350. | Brian Burrows | Bugsy |

JIMMY HILL

351. False

352. 1928

353. Crystal Palace

354. 1961

355. Match of the Day

356. The Sky Blue Song

357. Professional Footballers Association

358. Brentford and Fulham

359. 1963/1964

360. True

BRIAN BORROWS

361. Bolton Wanderers

362. 1960

363. Defender

364. Manchester City

365. Don Mackay

366. 41

367. Everton

368. West Ham United

369. Two

370. Swindon Town

NOEL CANTWELL

371. 1967

372. Full-back

373. Sixth

374. 25

375. Bob Dennison

376. Bayern Munich

377. Tenth

378. True

379. 36

380. 1972

AWAY DAYS - 3

381. Wigan Athletic

382. Crewe Alexandra

383. Brentford

384. Carlisle United

385. Bradford City

386. Charlton Athletic

387. Crystal Palace

388. Bristol City

389. Cheltenham Town

390. Canvey Island

MIXED BAG - 1

391. Floodlight failure

392. Nicky Platnauer

393. Jerry Best (236 appearances from 1920-26)

394. Brian Kilcline

395. Dele Adebola (the other was Neil 'Razor' Ruddock)

396. Miner

397. Queens Park Rangers (20 August 2005, City won 3-0)

398. 19

399. Leicester City

400. Gary Breen

JOE MERCER

401.	Everton and Arsenal
402.	Manchester City
403.	OBE
404.	19th
405.	Crystal Palace and Manchester City
406.	1914
407.	Five
408.	Manchester City
409.	Tottenham Hotspur
410.	Left

FORMER OCCUPATIONS

411.	Mo Konjic	Train Driver
412.	Stuart Pearce	Electrician
413.	Dave Bamber	Economics Graduate
414.	George Curtis	Miner
415.	Thomas Gustafsson	Ice Hockey Player
416.	Steve Ogrizovic	Policeman
417.	Colin Dobson	Shipyard Engineer
418.	Ernie Hunt	Gravedigger
419.	Andy Williams	Accountant
420.	David Busst	Financial Adviser

GARY GILLESPIE

421.	Falkirk
422.	17
423.	1978
424.	£75,000
425.	Middlesbrough
426.	Liverpool

427.   Andy Roxburgh

428.   The European Cup

429.   Glasgow Celtic

430.   1994

RON ATKINSON

431.   Phil Neal

432.   Big Ron

433.   1995 (February)

434.   West Ham United

435.   Kevin Richardson

436.   True

437.   Director of Football

438.   Oxford United

439.   True

440.   Kettering Town (1971-1974), Cambridge United (1974-1978) and West Bromwich Albion (1978-1981)

DEBUTS

441.   David Thompson

442.   Gordon Milne

443.   Ashley Grimes, Micky Gynn, Dave Bamber, Nicky Platnauer and Terry Gibson

444.   Terry Gibson

445.   Martin Jol

446.   Phil Babb

447.   Paul Heald

448.   True

449.   Sam Allardyce

450.   Tottenham Hotspur

JOHN SILLETT

451.   Chelsea

452.   Charles

453.   Full-back

454.   Jimmy Hill

455.   One

456.   Plymouth Argyle

457.   Hereford United

458.   Terry Butcher

459.   Tenth

460.   True

LEAGUE APPEARANCES - 2

461.	Micky Quinn	64
462.	Darren Huckerby	94
463.	Peter Ndlovu	141
464.	Dennis Wise	13
465.	Phil Babb	77
466.	John Aloisi	47
467.	Craig Bellamy	34
468.	Tommy Hutchison	314
469.	David Phillips	100
470.	Ernie Hunt	146

NICKNAMES - 2

471.	Moustapha Hadji	Detonator
472.	Les Warner	Plum
473.	Steve Staunton	Stan
474.	Frank Herbert	Cute
475.	John Williams	Flying Postman
476.	Peter Ndlovu	Bulawayo Bullet

477.	John Sillett	Snoz
478.	Brian Roberts	Harry
479.	Ray Straw	Toffee
480.	Mick Coop	The Scoop

CHRIS CATTLIN

481. Lancashire

482. John

483. Huddesfield Town

484. 1968

485. Noel Cantwell

486. 1976

487. Brighton & Hove Albion

488. None

489. Mick Channon

490. Brighton & Hove Albion

HAT-TRICKS

491. Gary McSheffrey

492. Preston North End

493. Macclesfield Town (FA Cup) and Nottingham Forest (Premier League)

494. Lee Hughes

495. Dion Dublin

496. Peter Ndlovu

497. None

498. Bobby Gould

499. Two

500. Jim Melrose

SKY BLUE CRICKETERS

501. Steve Ogrizovic

502. *Freddie Gardner*

503. *Arthur Jepson*

504. *Don Bennett*

505. *Patsy Hendren*

506. *Charlie Elliott*

507. *Bryan Richardson*

508. *John Mitten*

509. *Jack Lee*

510. *Robert Turner*

MATCH THE YEAR - 2

511.	Dele Adebola scored on his Coventry debut against Peterborough United	2003
512.	Coventry sold Craig Bellamy to Newcastle United for £6.5 million	2001
513.	Coventry beat Wolves 7-1 at home on Christmas Day	1922
514.	Coventry moved to the Rioch Arena	2005
515.	Ken Hale scored for the Sky Blues against Bristol Rovers after just 7 seconds	1964
516.	Coventry lost 8-1 at home to Leicester City in the League Cup	1964
517.	David Bell signed for Coventry City	2009
518.	Coventry paid Blackburn Rovers £2.5 million for Lee Carsley	2000
519.	George Curtis took over as Coventry manager	1986
520.	Peter Reid left Coventry having managed them for only 31 games	2005

MICKY ADAMS

521. *1961*

522. Full-back

523. Gillingham

524. Tottenham Hotspur

525. Everton

526. Three

527. 1987

528. 8th

529. 2005

530. Newcastle United

DAVE BENNETT

531. Manchester City

532. 1983

533. 172

534. 1989

535. Sheffield Wednesday

536. Swindon Town

537. 25

538. Shrewsbury Town

539. Cardiff City

540. Nuneaton Borough

WHO ARE WE PLAYING? - 3

541. Sunderland

542. Crewe Alexandra

543. Bristol City

544. Grimsby Town

545. Canvey Island

546. Fulham

547. Manchester City

548. Colchester United and Oxford United

549.   Mansfield Town

550.   Dagenham & Redbridge

MICK FERGUSON

551.   Striker

552.   127

553.   Birmingham City

554.   Everton

555.   54

556.   Brighton & Hove Albion

557.   1971

558.   Colchester United

559.   1981

560.   Wealdstone FC

POSITIONS IN THE LEAGUE - 2

561.	1987/1988	10th in Division One
562.	1985/1986	17th in Division One
563.	1983/1984	19th in Division One
564.	1981/1982	14th in Division One
565.	1979/1980	15th in Division One
566.	1977/1978	7th in Division One
567.	1975/1976	14th in Division One
568.	1973/1974	16th in Division One
569.	1971/1972	18th in Division One
570.	1969/1970	6th in Division One

FORMER AWAY GROUNDS

571.   Manchester City

572.   Leicester City

573.   Arsenal

574. **Middlesbrough**

575. **Wimbledon**

576. **Brighton & Hove Albion**

577. **Sunderland**

578. **Southampton**

579. **Reading**

580. **Derby County**

POT LUCK – 1

581. **Charity Shield**

582. **None**

583. **Perry Suckling**

584. **Wycombe Wanderers**

585. **York City**

586. **Jimmy Holmes**

587. **Terry Butcher (appointed November 1990)**

588. **Colin Stein (the reporter swore on air when Stein missed a chance to score in a game for Glasgow Rangers)**

589. **Noel Cantwell, Noel Simpson and Noel Whelan**

590. **Jerry Best**

MIXED BAG – 2

591. **Mick Quinn (he scored in six successive Premier League games in 1992-93, bagging nine goals)**

592. **Jerry Best**

593. **Phil Neal**

594. **Roy Barry**

595. **Electrician**

596. **2005 (20 August 2005)**

597. **Kevin Richardson (February 1995)**

598. **Hull City (24 September 2005, Hull City won 2-0)**

599. Hartlepools United (now called Hartlepool United, City won 5-2)

600. Jackie Brown

POT LUCK – 2

601. Cheltenham Town and Yeovil Town

602. Aston Villa and Liverpool

603. Gary McAllister

604. George Raynor

605. Gordon Strachan

606. Cyrille Regis

607. Brian Clough

608. UEFA Cup Winners' Cup (European ban on English teams entering Europe due to Heysel disaster in 1985)

609. Ipswich Town

610. Kevin Keegan (won the Ballon D'Or in 1978 and 1979)

1970s

611. Gordon Milne

612. Birmingham City and Luton Town

613. David Cross

614. Jeff Blockley

615. Trakia Plovdiv

616. 19th

617. True

618. Bobby McDonald

619. Chris Chattlin (away against Everton) and Ernie Hunt (at home against Liverpool)

620. Everton

ERNIE HUNT

621. Roger (Roger Patrick, adopted Ernie after his father and to

prevent confusion with Liverpool and England's Roger Hunt)

622.   Swindon Town

623.   Wolverhampton Wanderers

624.   1968

625.   Everton

626.   £80,000

627.   Doncaster Rovers

628.   Five (1968-73)

629.   Bristol City

630.   Los Angeles Wolves

WHERE DID THEY GO - 2

631.	Trevor Benjamin	Peterborough United
632.	Andy Marriott	Colchester United
633.	Barry Quinn	Oxford United
634.	Scott Shearer	Bristol Rovers
635.	Mo Konjic	Derby County
636.	Jay Boothroyd	Perugia
637.	Youssef Safri	Norwich City
638.	Steve Staunton	Walsall
639.	Julian Joachim	Leeds United
640.	Craig Pead	Walsall

TOMMY HUTCHISON

641.   Alloa Athletic

642.   Blackpool

643.   1972

644.   Bob Stokoe

645.   Billy Rafferty

646.   1980

647.   Manchester City

648. West Germany 1974

649. Swansea City

650. Manchester City and an own goal for Tottenham Hotspur in the 1981 FA Cup Final

JIM BLYTH

651. Preston North End

652. 1972

653. Manchester United

654. 151

655. Hereford United

656. 1982

657. Birmingham City

658. Gordon Strachan

659. Chris Kirkland

660. Glasgow Celtic

POT LUCK – 3

661. Jimmy Holmes

662. Wolverhampton Wanderers (7-1 at Highfield Road in Division Two, 1922)

663. Nii Lamptey

664. Alf Wood

665. Winston Churchill (The Winston Churchill Trophy)

666. Fulham and West Ham United

667. Mo Konjic

668. One (Arthur Bacon 1934-37)

669. Bobby Gould

670. George Curtis

DAVE CLEMENTS

671. Portadown

672. Wolverhampton Wanderers

673. Jimmy Hill

674. Northampton Town

675. Seven (1964-71)

676. 255

677. Sheffield Wednesday

678. Everton

679. New York Cosmos

680. Northern Ireland

IAN WALLACE

681. Glasgow

682. Dumbarton

683. 1976

684. £80,000

685. Gordon Milne

686. Mick Ferguson

687. Nottingham Forest

688. 1

689. Sunderland

690. Jim Blyth

THE BIRMINGHAM CITY CONNECTION - 1

691.	Peter Ndlovu	1991-97
692.	Tommy Briggs	1950-51
693.	Fred Hawley	1919-20
694.	Gerry Daly	1980-84
695.	Kevin Drinkell	1989-92
696.	David Smith	1988-93
697.	Tony Hateley	1988-89
698.	David Burrows	1995-2000

| 699. | Jackie Randle | 1922-27 |
| 700. | Bill Bradbury | 1950-54 |

HONOURS

701.	FA Cup Winners	1987
702.	Division Three (South) Champions	1936
703.	FA Youth Cup Runners-up	1999
704.	Division Four Runners-up	1959
705.	FA Youth Cup Runners-up	1968
706.	Division Two Champions	1967
707.	FA Youth Cup Winners	1987
708.	FA Youth Cup Runners-up	1970
709.	Division Three Champions	1964
710.	FA Youth Cup Runners-up	2000

GARY BREEN

711. Charlton Athletic
712. Maidstone United
713. Gillingham
714. Peterborough United
715. £2.5 million
716. West Ham United
717. Sunderland
718. Wolverhampton Wanderers
719. Mick McCarthy
720. 63

RICHARD SHAW

721. Defender
722. One
723. Millwall

724.   1968

725.   Crystal Palace

726.   1998/1999 and 2002/2003

727.   Ron Atkinson

728.   True: playing for Crystal Palace against Manchester United

729.   37: 36 and one substitute appearance

730.   Hull City

AWAY DAYS - 4

731.   Chelsea

732.   Derby County

733.   Chesterfield

734.   Chester City

735.   Crawley Town

736.   Accrington Stanley

737.   Forest Green Rovers

738.   Burnley

739.   Colchester United

740.   Dagenham & Redbridge

WHO ARE WE PLAYING? - 4

741.   Lincoln City

742.   Nottingham Forest

743.   Derby County

744.   Doncaster Rovers

745.   Huddersfield Town

746.   Crystal Palace

747.   Ipswich Town

748.   Hartlepool United

749.   Macclesfield Town

750.   Gravesend & Northfleet

WHICH POSITION - 1

751.	Peter Atherton	Defender
752.	Chris Kirkland	Goalkeeper
753.	Danny Thomas	Defender
754.	Noel Whelan	Striker
755.	Cyrille Regis	Striker
756.	Colin Hawkins	Defender
757.	Richard Shaw	Defender
758.	Mark Hateley	Striker
759.	Bill Glazier	Goalkeeper
760.	Willie Boland	Defender

WHERE DID THEY COME FROM - 3

761.	Darren Huckerby	Newcastle United
762.	Lee Hughes	West Bromwich Albion
763.	Laurent Delorge	Ghent
764.	Dimitrios Konstantopoulos	Hartlepool United
765.	Regis Genaux	Liège
766.	Ranar Normann	Lillestrom
767.	Paul Telfer	Luton Town
768.	Dion Dublin	Manchester United
769.	Robert Jarni	Seville
770.	Eion Jess	Aberdeen

MIXED BAG – 3

771. Chelsea beat Leeds United in the replay at Old Trafford

772. Eric Black

773. Eddy Brown

774. Peter Reid

775. Charlie Elliott

776. £113m

777. A heavy snowfall (City were losing 2-0 at the time but won the re-arranged game 3-2)

778. Don Dorman

779. David Rennie

780. Ernie Machin

AWAY DAYS - 5

781. Fulham

782. Ipswich Town

783. Doncaster Rovers

784. Grimsby Town

785. Exeter City

786. Bolton Wanderers

787. Leeds United

788. Gillingham

789. Leyton Orient

790. Darlington

WHERE DID THEY GO - 3

791.	Dele Adebola	Bristol City
792.	Robert Page	Huddersfield Town
793.	Gary McSheffrey	Birmingham City
794.	Colin Cameron	MK Dons
795.	Stephen Hughes	Walsall
796.	Andrew Whing	Brighton & Hove Albion
797.	Andy Morrell	Blackpool
798.	Ryan Lynch	Crewe Alexandra
799.	Kevin Pressman	Mansfield Town
800.	James Scowcroft	Crystal Palace

PLAYER OF THE YEAR

801.	Willie Carr	1972/1973

802.	Graham Oakey	1974/1975
803.	Tommy Hutchison	1975/1976
804.	Gary Gillespie	1979/1980
805.	Nicky Platnauer	1983/1984
806.	Steve Ogrizovic	1986/1987
807.	Kevin Gallacher	1990/1991
808.	Peter Atherton	1992/1993
809.	Brian Borrows	1994/1995
810.	Gary McAllister	1999/2000

WHO ARE WE PLAYING? - 5

811. Manchester United
812. Luton Town
813. Exeter City
814. Leyton Orient
815. Grays Athletic
816. Portsmouth
817. Millwall
818. Darlington
819. Northampton Town
820. Halifax Town

WHICH POSITION - 2

821.	Bryan King	Goalkeeper
822.	Ellery Cairo	Midfielder
823.	Gary Breen	Defender
824.	Steve Whitton	Striker
825.	Michael Hughes	Midfielder
826.	Colin Hendry	Defender
827.	Steve Sedgley	Midfielder
828.	Les Sealey	Goalkeeper

| 829. | Trevor Peake | Midfielder |
| 830. | John Hartson | Striker |

CYRILLE REGIS

831.	1984
832.	Tottenham Hotspur
833.	1-1
834.	Striker
835.	Five
836.	12 goals
837.	MBE
838.	Sheffield Wednesday
839.	47
840.	Aston Villa and Wolves

THE BIRMINGHAM CITY CONNECTION - 2

841.	David Rennie	1993-96
842.	John Gayle	1993-94
843.	Frank Crowe	1919-20
844.	Fred Gardner	1945-49
845.	Gary Breen	1997-2002
846.	Don Dearson	1947-50
847.	William Morgan	1920-22
848.	Ken Rowley	1954-55
849.	Liam Daish	1996-97
850.	Chris Whyte	1995

1992/1993 – FIRST PREMIER LEAGUE SEASON

851.	Bobby Gould
852.	Steve Orgizovic and Jonathan Gould
853.	Mick Quinn

854.   *Peter Atherton*

855.   *True*

856.   *Tottenham Hotspur*

857.   *15th*

858.   *John Williams*

859.   *5-1*

860.   *John Williams, Mick Quinn and Peter Ndlovu*

HARRY BARRATT

861.   *Southampton*

862.   *Christmas Day (1919)*

863.   *1934*

864.   *Cheltenham Town*

865.   *Blackburn Rovers*

866.   *Left Back (he once replaced Alf Wood in goal)*

867.   *Chief Scout*

868.   *Gillingham*

869.   *176*

870.   *12*

TREVOR PEAKE

871.   *Nuneaton Town*

872.   *1983*

873.   *Lincoln City*

874.   *1991*

875.   *Luton Town*

876.   *1998*

877.   *Gordon Strachan*

878.   *2002*

879.   *Roland Nilsson*

880.   *Steve Ogrizovic*

BOBBY GOULD

881. *Two: 1983/1984 and 1992/1993*

882. *Striker*

883. *Anthony*

884. *1968*

885. *Arsenal*

886. *Jimmy Hill*

887. *Nottingham Forest*

888. *15th*

889. *Phil Neal*

890. *Wales*

MICK QUINN

891. *Bobby Gould*

892. *Manchester City*

893. *Arsenal*

894. *Liverpool*

895. *Oldham Athletic*

896. *26*

897. *Who Ate All The pies*

898. *Everton*

899. *False: Peter Atherton won the award*

900. *Eight*

MIXED BAG – 4

901. *George Curtis*

902. *Jim Blyth*

903. *98,000 (the 1987 Final versus Tottenham Hotspur at Wembley Stadium)*

904. *Ron Atkinson (February 1995)*

905. *Claus Bech Jørgensen*

906.   *Faroe Islands*

907.   *32, 0000*

908.   *Crewe Alexandra*

909.   *Noel Cantwell*

910.   *Adrian Heath*

POSITIONS IN THE LEAGUE - 3

911.	*1967/1968*	*20th in Division One*
912.	*1969/1970*	*6th in Division One*
913.	*1978/1979*	*10th in Division One*
914.	*1981/1982*	*14th in Division One*
915.	*1985/1986*	*18th in Division One*
916.	*1989/1990*	*12th in Division One*
917.	*1994/1995*	*16th in the Premier League*
918.	*1998/1999*	*15th in the Premier League*
919.	*1999/2000*	*14th in the Premier League*
920.	*2004/2005*	*19th in the Championship*

CONSECUTIVE SCORERS

921.	*Mick Quinn*	*9 goals in 6 games (1992)*
922.	*Dave Clements*	*5 goals in 5 games (1965)*
923.	*Andy Morrell*	*5 goals in 5 games (2003)*
924.	*Bobby Gould*	*6 goals in 6 games (1967)*
925.	*Terry Bly*	*9 goals in 7 games (1962)*
926.	*Clarrie Bourton*	*19 goals in 10 games (1931)*
927.	*Darren Huckerby*	*4 goals in 2 games (1999)*
928.	*Elliott Ward*	*4 goals in 3 games (2008)*
929.	*Stern John*	*4 goals in 3 games (2005)*
930.	*Cedric Roussel*	*3 goals in 2 games (2000)*

GORDON STRACHAN

931.   *1995*

932. Scottish

933. Five

934. Midfielder

935. True

936. 40

937. 15th

938. Ron Atkinson

939. False: he never scored for Coventry City

940. Southampton

WILLIE CARR

941. Glasgow

942. 1967

943. The Donkey Kick

944. Everton

945. Ernie Hunt

946. Arsenal

947. 1975

948. Wolverhampton Wanderers

949. A League Cup winners' medal

950. Millwall

LOAN PLAYERS

951.	Ian Bennett	Birmingham City
952.	Luke Steele	Manchester United
953.	Johnnie Jackson	Tottenham Hotspur
954.	Lee Sawyer	Chelsea
955.	Paul Trollope	Fulham
956.	Tim Flowers	Leicester City
957.	Jordan Henderson	Sunderland
958.	Matt Jansen	Blackburn Rovers

| 959. | Kasper Schmeichel | Manchester City |
| 960. | Richie Partridge | Liverpool |

GARRY THOMPSON

961. Striker

962. West Bromwich Albion

963. Gordon Milne

964. Lindsey

965. 10

966. Sunderland

967. Leeds United

968. Middlesbrough

969. Two

970. 1959

DION DUBLIN

971. Queens Park Rangers

972. True

973. 1994

974. 13

975. Four

976. 1996/1997 and 1997/1998

977. Leicester City

978. Sheffield Wednesday

979. Southampton

980. Aston Villa

SKY BLUE AUTHORS

981.	Ron Atkinson	A Different Ball Game
982.	George Raynor	Football Ambassador At Large
983.	Jimmy Hill	Football Crazy

984.	Harry Barratt	Crown Green Bowls: The Rules Of The Game
985.	Mark Hateley	Top Mark
986.	Gary McAllister	Captain's Log
987.	Phil Neal	Attack From The Back
988.	Terry Yorath	Hard Man, Hard Knocks
989.	Joe Mercer	The Great Ones
990.	Mick Quinn	Who Ate All The Pies?

GORDON MILNE

991. Preston North End
992. Liverpool
993. Bill Shankly
994. Blackpool
995. Wigan Athletic
996. 1972
997. Joe Mercer
998. 1974
999. Leicester City
1000. Beşiktaş

NOTES:

NOTES:

NOTES:

NOTES:

NOTES:

OTHER BOOKS BY CHRIS COWLIN:

* Celebrities' Favourite Football Teams

* The British TV Sitcom Quiz Book

* The Cricket Quiz Book

* The Gooners Quiz Book

* The Horror Film Quiz Book

* The Official Aston Villa Quiz Book

* The Official Birmingham City Quiz Book

* The Official Brentford Quiz Book

* The Official Bristol Rovers Quiz Book

* The Official Burnley Quiz Book

* The Official Bury Quiz Book

* The Official Carlisle United Quiz Book

* The Official Carry On Quiz Book

* The Official Chesterfield Football Club Quiz Book

* The Official Colchester United Quiz Book

* The Official Doncaster Rovers Quiz Book

* The Official Greenock Morton Quiz Book

* The Official Heart of Midlothian Quiz Book

* The Official Hereford United Quiz Book

* The Official Hull City Quiz Book

OTHER BOOKS BY CHRIS COWLIN:

* The Official Leicester City Quiz Book

* The Official Macclesfield Town Quiz Book

* The Official Norwich City Football Club Quiz

* The Official Notts County Quiz Book

* The Official Peterborough United Quiz Book

* The Official Port Vale Quiz Book

* The Official Rochdale AFC Quiz Book

* The Official Rotherham United Quiz Book

* The Official Shrewsbury Town Quiz Book

* The Official Stockport County Quiz Book

* The Official Watford Football Club Quiz Book

* The Official West Bromwich Albion Quiz Book

* The Official Wolves Quiz Book

* The Official Yeovil Town Quiz Book

* The Reality Television Quiz Book

* The Southend United Quiz Book

* The Sunderland AFC Quiz Book

* The Ultimate Derby County Quiz Book

* The West Ham United Quiz Book

www.apexpublishing.co.uk